12 50

The MIDI Programmer's Handbook

M&T BOOKS

The MIDI Programmer's Handbook

Steve De Furia
and
Joe Scacciaferro

Ferro Technologies

M&T Publishing, Inc.
Redwood City, California

M & T Books
A Division of M & T Publishing, Inc.
501 Galveston Drive
Redwood City, CA 94063

M & T Books
General Manager, Linda Hanger
Acquisitions Editor, Brenda McLaughlin
Operations Manager, Michelle Hudun
Senior Project Editor, Dave Rosenthal
Assistant Project Editor, Kurt Rosenthal
Cover Art Director, Michael Hollister
Cover Designer, Lisa Schneider

Ferro Technologies
Software Design, Steve De Furia
Editor, Barbara Williams
Design and Production, everon enterprises
Illustrator, Steve De Furia

The MIDI Programmer's Handbook
Library of Congress Number 89-043676

ISBN 1-55851-068-0
$24.95

92 91 90 89   4 3 2 1

Limits of Liability and Disclaimer of Warranty

Acknowledgements

All terms mentioned in this book that are known to be trademarks or service marks are listed below. In addition, terms suspected of being trademarks or service marks have been appropriately capitalized. M&T Books cannot attest to the accuracy of this information. Use of a term in this book should not be regarded as affecting the validity of any trademark or service mark.

Macintosh is a trademark of Apple Computer Inc.
Atari ST is a trademark of Atari Corp.
DMP 11, WX 7, and C 1 are trademarks of Yamaha Music Corp.
M1 is a trademark of Korg USA
LXP-5 is a trademark of Lexicon, Inc.
VZ-8M and PG-380 are trademarks of Casio Inc.
D-50, MC-500, and R-8 are trademarks of Roland Corp.

"Standard MIDI Files 1.0", The International MIDI Association (July, 1988) reprinted by permission.

Contents

Part One

Basic Concepts

Part One

Basic Concepts

Introduction

The MIDI Programmer's Handbook is a complete and indispensable reference for anyone writing MIDI software or working with MIDI on a technical level. The book is divided into four major parts: Parts One and Two will help you understand what MIDI is, and how it is used. Part Three contains a complete technical description of every defined MIDI message, as well as detailed implementation notes. Part Four demonstrates the design of real-time MIDI software applications. A brief summary of each part follows.

Part One: Basic Concepts
This section is for programmers who haven't had much hands-on experience with MIDI applications. It focuses on the basic functions of MIDI devices and the way in which these devices are configured into systems. A special section on synchronization explains how to link MIDI devices to audio and video recorders using MIDI, SMPTE Time code, MIDI Time Code, and FSK synchronization techniques.

Part Two: MIDI in the Real World
Any MIDI device will implement only a subset of all possible MIDI features and functions. This section explains how to read MIDI Implementation Charts to find out what MIDI capabilities your software can access on a particular device. Actual charts are included for several typical devices such as stand-alone synthesizers, sequencers, audio effects, and tone modules, etc.

Part Three: MIDI Programmer's Reference
This section is a programmer's MIDI dictionary which includes a summary for every defined MIDI message. Each summary contains a hexadecimal/binary listing of the bytes that make up the message and a detailed explanation of usage and special cases. The information that you'll need most often has been organized into convenient reference charts and tables. Also included in this section, are detailed notes and illustrations covering such topics as Running Status transmission format, MIDI modes, MIDI Clock and MIDI Time Code commands, Sample Dump Standard communication protocols, and the MIDI Files Standard.

Part Four: Writing MIDI Software

A "generic" real-time MIDI application is developed in this section. The program gives examples and guidelines for how to identify, recognize, or ignore any MIDI message received from your computer's MIDI In port. The program can echo incoming messages directly to the MIDI Out port, or it can trap and process selected messages before sending them out. The example demonstrates many of the fundamentals of MIDI software design including: receiving Running Status transmission format, handling prioritized System Real-Time messages, parsing messages by type, parsing messages by byte, decoding multi-byte MIDI values, processing Channel Voice messages, and processing System Exclusive messages. All of the major algorithms used in the overall shell and in the individual routines are thoroughly described. To simplify translation of the program into the language of your choice, the code examples are given in both English and Pascal.

MIDI Basics

MIDI is a communications protocol originally created for interfacing synthesizers and other electronic musical instruments. It has evolved into a communication pipeline that can link virtually all of the equipment used in music and video production. MIDI allows devices to pass "messages" back and forth. These messages can transfer several different types of control and data values. Some of the information that can be passed in MIDI messages is listed below.

- Real-time performance controls — which notes are played, how loudly or softly they are played, which controllers (pedals, wheels, switches, breath pressure, etc.) are moved

- Metronome timing reference — time in musical beats

- Absolute timing reference — time in hours, minutes, seconds, and frames

- Universal parameters and data — sample sound data and parameters that can be used by any MIDI device

- Device-specific parameters and data — virtually any kind of information can be passed between similar devices, without "confusing" other devices in the system

All of the performance-related messages can be assigned to any of MIDI's 16 independent channels. This is one of the most powerful features of MIDI. It makes it possible to transmit as many as 16 independent, polyphonic performances over a single cable. MIDI instruments can be set to receive only on a given channel, so each of those 16 performances can be routed from its source to 16 different instruments, each with its own unique sound.

Anatomy of a MIDI Instrument

Electronic musical instruments consist of a set of subsystems linked together by a mircoprocessor. A typical instrument (such as a synthesizer or sampler) consists of performance controllers — keyboard, wheels, levers, pedals, and so on, voice circuitry — memory for storing preset sound *programs*, and front-panel controls — for such instrument specific tasks as programming the sounds and setting operation modes. There are no direct connections between individual subsystems. Instead, they communicate through a built-in microprocessor. For example, the keyboard electronics are not hard-wired to the voice circuits. When a key is played, a digital signal is sent from the keyboard to the microprocessor. The microprocessor receives this signal and assigns it to the voice circuits. The same type of thing occurs when a front panel control or memory selection button is moved. A digital signal is sent from the control to the microprocessor, and the processor routes the signal to the appropriate circuitry.

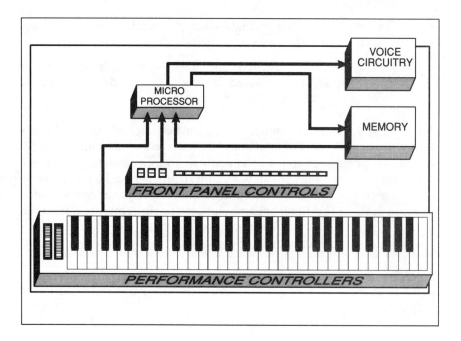

The modular design of these instruments means that it's not necessary for all of the subsystems to be in the same physical package. There's no reason for the keyboard and voice circuits to be integrated into one unit. The keyboard can be physically separate from the voice circuitry; the two microprocessor-based modules simply require a cable between them. Once the keyboard has been separated from the voice circuits, it isn't necessary to connect a particular keyboard to a particular voice module. If voice modules can interpret the keyboard's signals, they become interchangeable. Different kinds of keyboard modules can be used too, as long as they all produce the same signals when they are played in the same way.

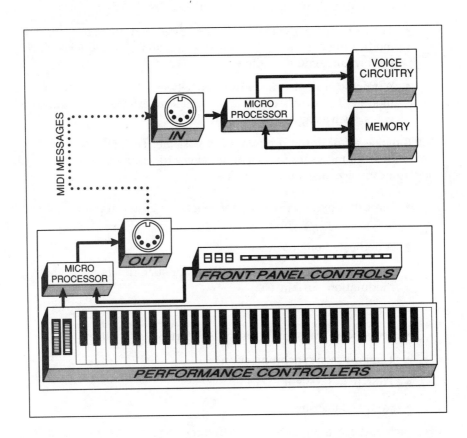

Once we have signals flowing out of a keyboard and into a voice module, other interesting things can happen.

- The signals can be duplicated and sent simultaneously to more than one voice module.

- A recording device can be inserted between the keyboard and the voice module. It can capture the signals, preserving their timing and sequence in its memory (similar to the way a player piano captures a keyboard performance on a piano roll). Later, the recording device can play back the signals to recreate the performance. (This recreation can control the same or a different voice module.)

- The recorded performance can be edited in a number of ways to modify the playback. For example, the tempo or sequence of the performance could be altered.

- A processing device can be inserted between the keyboard and voice module. This device can alter the signals in real-time in a number of ways, such as by harmonizing melodies.

MIDI makes all of this and much more possible. The MIDI specification defines a set of messages for just about every function that is common to electronic musical instruments, such as:

- More than ten octaves of discrete pitches (128), with optional velocity and pressure dynamics for each note

- A dedicated pitch bender

- A group of 95 real-time controllers for such functions as volume, modulation, sustain, etc.

- Memory selection

- Sequencer "transport" controls — Start, Stop, Continue

- Tempo-based synchronization

- Time-based synchronization

- Sample data transfer

For each of these, a separate set of MIDI messages has been defined. The message definitions specify the exact signals each controller should transmit when played, and exactly how these signals should be responded to when received. Messages have also been defined to handle other functions like program selection (memory access), and sequencer operation and timing. There is also a set of MIDI messages that allow device-specific information, such as data dumps, to be transferred between similar instruments, or between an instrument and a computer. The most recently defined set of messages are those for MIDI Time Code. These messages are used to link MIDI instruments with a time-based synchronization standard. There are currently more than 100 defined MIDI messages. Furthermore, since the specification is open-ended, messages for new functions can be added to the specification. In the future, there may be MIDI messages defined for console automation, machine transport control, and any number of other functions that fall within the scope of music/audio/video production.

Anatomy of a MIDI System

MIDI also defines the way in which instruments can be connected. The basic rule is that at any given time, there can be only one device transmitting messages, but there can be more than one device receiving messages. Receiving instruments can be made "channel selective" so that they will recognize only messages transmitted on an assigned channel. Since there are 16 channels defined by MIDI, it is possible for a single device to transmit different sets of messages to as many as 16 different MIDI instruments at once.

Master/Slave

This is the simplest possible MIDI system, one instrument (the master) controls another (the slave).

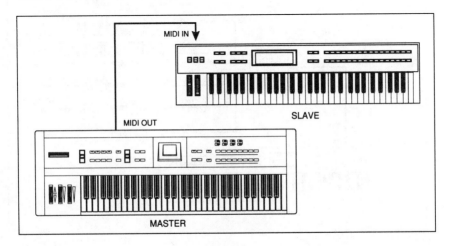

Multiple Slaves

The MIDI Thru port makes it possible to send duplicate copies of the master's MIDI messages to additional instruments. When no more than three slaves are used, a daisy-chain hook-up, as shown in the first drawing below, will work fine. If four or more slaves are in the system, a Thru box is recommended, as shown in the second drawing.

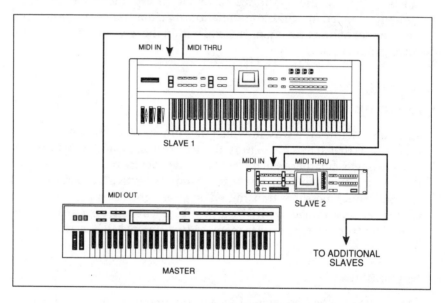

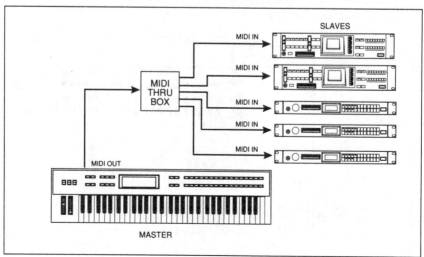

Multiple Channels

A master can transmit over as many as 16 independent channels at the same time via a single MIDI cable.

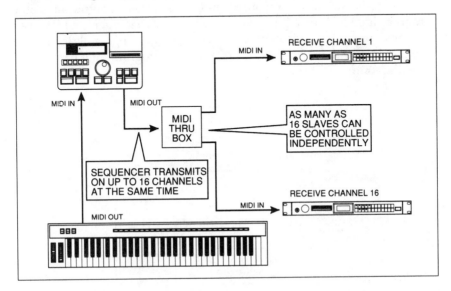

Each slave in a system can be set to respond to only a particular channel, or to a particular range of channels.

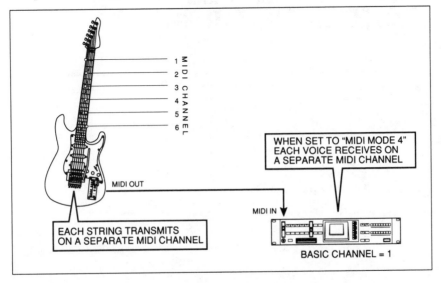

Merged Masters

In some situations, it may be necessary to connect two masters to one slave. For example, you might want to connect a tone module (a slave-only device with no keyboard) to a keyboard and a computer running an editor program. In such cases a special device, called a MIDI merger, could be used to combine the MIDI outputs of both masters, making it possible to play the tone module from the keyboard, and to edit its programming parameters from the computer at the same time.

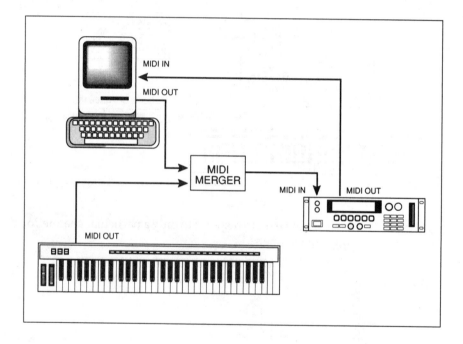

The Computer/MIDI Connection

Where does a computer fit into a MIDI system? Anywhere you want. It can be a generator, processor, or storage system for MIDI messages. You need a MIDI/computer interface and software for the desired applications. (As of this writing, two computers, the Yamaha C1 and the Atari ST, have built-in MIDI interfaces.) The most basic MIDI/computer interface provides a MIDI In port, and one or more MIDI Out ports. More sophisticated interfaces, such as the one shown below, may also provide other connections, such as additional MIDI In ports, tape sync in/out, and Time Code in/out. You can either buy existing MIDI software or create your own. In Part Four: Writing MIDI Software, we'll give you coding examples that show how to identify and process each type of MIDI message.

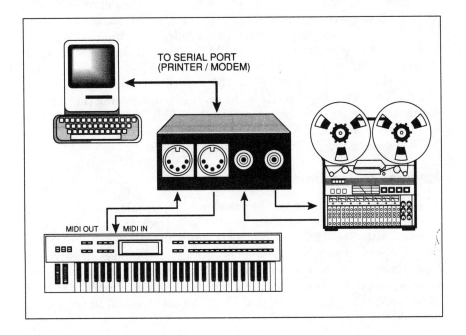

Synchronization Basics

Many MIDI applications involve synchronizing MIDI devices with each other, as well as with audio and video recorders. An overview of basic synchronization concepts and methods follows for those unfamiliar with such things as sync tones, clocks, and Time Code.

Audio tape recorders (ATRs), video tape recorders (VTRs), sequencers, and drum machines are used to record and play back a sequential flow of events. Whenever two or more of these devices are required to record or play simultaneously, they must be synchronized to a common timing reference. This ensures that each device will be precisely in time with the others. There are several different types of timing references and synchronization methods used. ATRs and VTRs are most commonly synchronized to SMPTE Time Code (a synchronization standard created by the Society of Motion Picture and Television Engineers). A device called a synchronizer is used to lock all of the recorders to a master SMPTE Time Code reference. MIDI sequencers and drum machines are commonly synchronized to MIDI Clocks, MIDI Time Code (MTC), an FSK "sync track," or to SMPTE Time Code. In situations where ATRs, VTRs, and MIDI devices must be synchronized, it is common practice to "translate" the SMPTE Time Code used to synchronize the recorders, into a timing reference that can synchronize the MIDI devices (either MIDI Timing Clocks or MTC).

Machine-to-Machine Synchronization

To synchronize two or more tape machines, one machine is used as the master and the others are used as slaves. A track of each machine is "striped" with SMPTE Time Code. This code is an audio signal that marks the passage of time in hours, minutes, seconds, and frames. In effect, the tape is branded with a continous stream of numbers. Each number corresponds to a physical location on the tape. There are two types of SMPTE Time Code, Longitudinal Time Code (LTC) and Vertical Interval Time Code (VITC).

LTC is recorded on a track of an ATR, or on the audio track of a VTR. VITC can only be recorded on VTRs, between frames of the video track. The information carried in each type of SMPTE Time Code is shown in the illustrations on the following two pages.

A significant technical difference between the two is that, with the right equipment, VITC can be read even if the VTR is stopped (freeze-frame), moving very slowly (scrub), or at high speeds (shuttle, rewind, fast forward). LTC cannot be read if the tape speed is very fast, very slow, or if the tape is stopped. The equipment needed to extract VITC from a video signal is quite expensive however, so in most music production situations the LTC format is used. If a VTR is used as the master, the LTC signal is recorded onto one of its audio tracks.

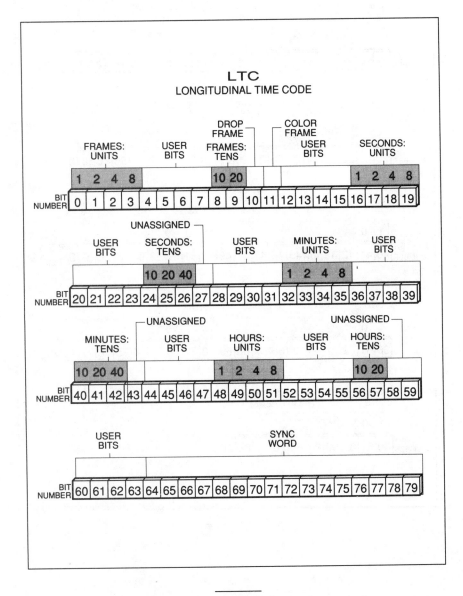

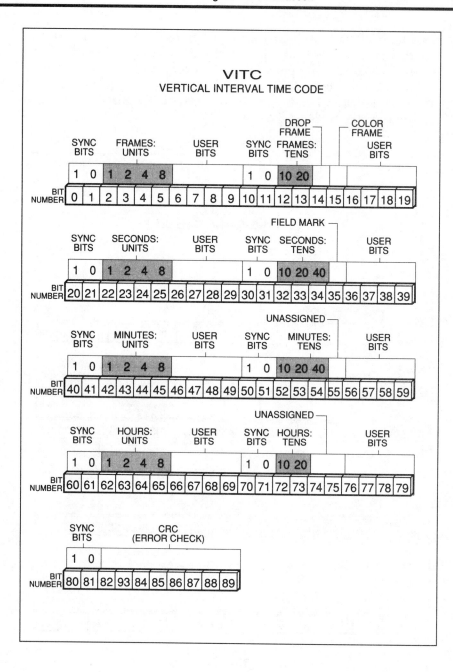

VITC

VERTICAL INTERVAL TIME CODE

The simplest way to synchronize machines to SMPTE Time code is to use a device called a synchronizer. One tape machine becomes the master and its SMPTE track is used as the master timing reference for all other machines. The synchronizer reads the SMPTE time from each slave and compares it to the master's time. If a slave is ahead of, or behind, the master time, the synchronizer slows it down or speeds it up to keep the two machines locked. (These changes in speed are too small to be noticeable.) The slaves are said to *chase* the master machine.

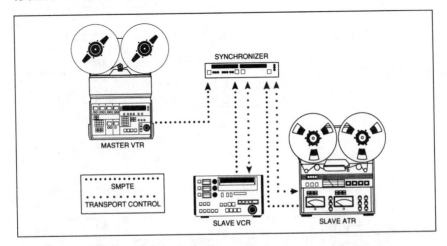

A more sophisticated SMPTE synchronization setup includes a device called a *locator*. The operator can enter a specific SMPTE address (like 01:23:45:00) into the locator, and it will move each connected device to the corresponding position on the tape.

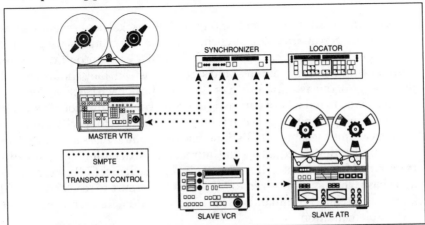

MIDI-to-MIDI Synchronization

To synchronize two or more MIDI devices, one device is used as the master and the others are used as slaves. The MIDI Out of the master is connected to the MIDI In of the slaves. MIDI provides two different timing references — MIDI Clocks and MIDI Time Code (MTC). The master will transmit one of these references through the MIDI cable to the slaves.

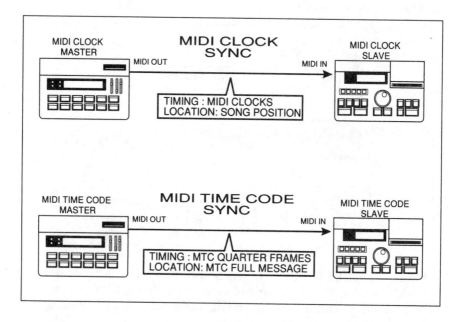

MIDI Clocks

MIDI Clocks are similar to a metronome or click-track. They are sent at a rate of 24 clocks per quarter-note, synchronized to the tempo setting of the master device. Unlike SMPTE Time Code, MIDI Clocks don't convey an absolute time in hours, minutes, and seconds. Instead, they simply convey the passage of one twenty-fourth of a musical beat. Each clock is identical. The only way to tell where you are is to keep a count of the clocks from the very beginning of the sequence. It is possible, however, to specify a location in musical time by using MIDI's Song Position Pointer message (SPP). This is a number that is equal to the number of sixteenth-notes since the beginning of the sequence. If a slave device can recognize SPPs, it can locate and chase when synchronized to MIDI Clocks. Be sure to read about MIDI Clocks and related commands in Part Three: System Real-Time messages and Implementation Notes.

MIDI Time Code

MIDI Time Code is based on SMPTE Time Code. Instead of transmitting messages timed to the tempo of the sequence, the master transmits messages that specify the passage of time in hours, minutes, seconds, and frames. Chase and locate functions are possible. Although MTC can be used to synchronize a MIDI-only setup, it is especially useful when MIDI devices need to be synchronized with tape machines synchronized to SMPTE Time Code.

MIDI-to-Machine

MIDI Clocks and MTC are transmitted through MIDI cables and can only be used to synchronize MIDI devices. Another timing reference must be used in applications where MIDI devices and ATRs or VTRs need to be synchronized in a single system. In virtually all of these applications, either an ATR or VTR will be used as the master. The timing reference coming from the master will be connected to an appropriate non-MIDI input on the MIDI device, or it will be converted to MIDI Clocks or MTC, then connected to the MIDI In port.

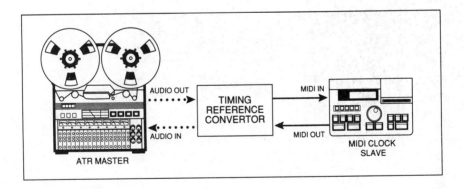

FSK Sync-to-Sequencer

One MIDI-to-machine method is the FSK (Frequency Sync Key) sync tone. An FSK tone is a series of audio frequency pulses that can be recorded onto any audio track of an ATR or VTR. The frequency pulses are sent at a rate equal to a timing interval relative to the quarter-note tempo of the music — for example, 96 pulses per quarter-note (ppq), 48 ppq, or 24 ppq. A track of the master recorder is striped with the FSK sync tone transmitted from the sync output of the MIDI device (usually labeled "sync-to-tape out" or "sync out"). Then the output of that track is connected to the appropriate input on the MIDI device (usually labeled "sync-to-tape in" or "sync in"). When the tape is played, the MIDI device counts the incoming pulses and keeps pace with them. Note that FSK tones don't carry any location information. The tape must always be started from the beginning of the music. Note also that the FSK sync track can't be used to synchronize other tape machines to the master machine. If this is necessary, a second track on the master will be striped with SMPTE, and the SMPTE track will be used to control the slave machines. Some MIDI devices don't have built-in FSK sync and require a sync-to-MIDI converter to synchronize with an FSK sync track.

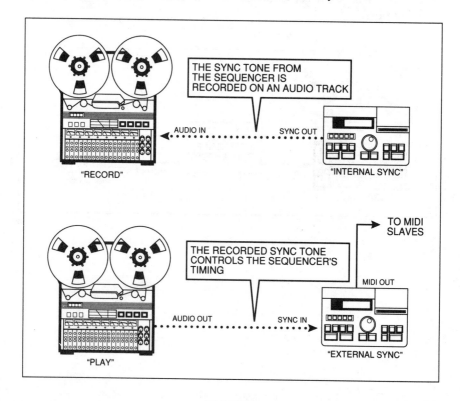

THE SYNC TONE FROM THE SEQUENCER IS RECORDED ON AN AUDIO TRACK

AUDIO IN   SYNC OUT

"RECORD"   "INTERNAL SYNC"

TO MIDI SLAVES

THE RECORDED SYNC TONE CONTROLS THE SEQUENCER'S TIMING

MIDI OUT

AUDIO OUT   SYNC IN

"PLAY"   "EXTERNAL SYNC"

SMPTE-to-Sequencer

Some MIDI sequencers have built-in dedicated SMPTE reader/generator hardware. With such a device, the SMTPE track of the master deck can be used as a timing reference for the sequencer. If an appropriate synchronizer is inserted between the master and the SMPTE sequencer, the sequencer can locate and chase the master recorder.

MIDI sequencers that don't have built-in SMPTE functions can be synchronized with SMPTE Time Code by using a SMPTE/MIDI Clock converter. This device reads the SMPTE track from the master and converts it to MIDI Clocks at the appropriate tempo. A feature of SMPTE/MIDI Clock converters is the ability to calculate and transmit SPP messages to the MIDI sequencer, allowing it to locate and chase the master recorder. As of this writing, these converters can process only the LTC format of SMPTE Time Code.

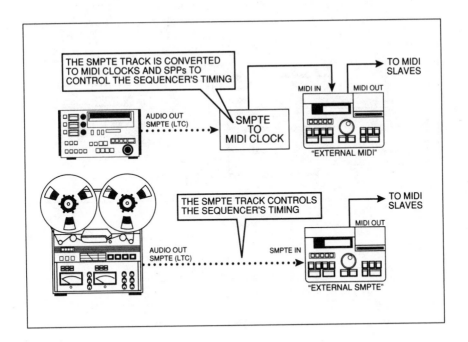

SMPTE-to-MTC

A SMPTE/MTC converter reads the SMPTE track from the synchronizer or master recorder and translates it to MTC messages that can be used to synchronize MIDI sequencers that recognize MTC. MTC and SMPTE correlate on a one-to-one basis, so locating a particular spot in an MTC sequence should be frame-accurate with the tape location. As of this writing, these converters can process only the MTC format of SMPTE Time Code.

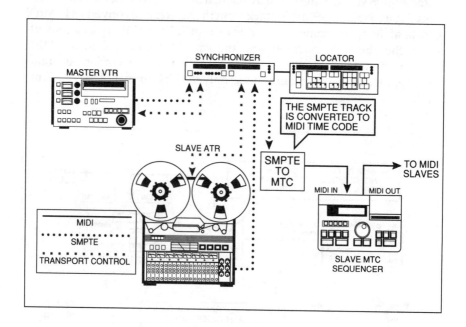

Part Two

MIDI in the Real World

Part Two

MIDI in the Real World

The MIDI Implementation

A particular MIDI device need not transmit or recognize every message defined by MIDI. (There are more than 100 messages defined in the current specification and additional messages are added as new uses for MIDI are identified.) A MIDI device need only transmit and recognize messages that are meaningful to its own particular functions. All other messages are simply ignored.

A *MIDI Implementation Chart* included in the owner's manual of any MIDI device lists the specific messages which are transmitted and recognized by that device. Although MIDI implementations vary, similar devices will have similar implementations. For example, you can expect all sound generators to recognize some range of MIDI's "Note On/Off" messages, while only those sound generators with a built-in keyboard (or similar controller) will transmit them. On the following page is a sample chart, followed by a set of guidelines to help you interpret other MIDI Implementation Charts.

MIDI Implementation Chart

Manufacuturer / Model
description: Example Chart

Date 11/21/89
Version: 0.1

Function . . .		Transmitted	Recognized	Remarks
Basic Channel	Default Changed	1 1-16	1 1-16	Memorized
Mode	Default Messages Altered	Mode 3 POLY OMNI OFF *************	Mode 1, 3, 4 MONO, POLY OMNI ON/OFF Mode 2 -> Mode 1	
Note Number:	True Voice	12-108 **************	0-127 12-108	
Velocity	Note ON Note OFF	O X 9n v = 0	O v = 1-127 X	
After Touch	Key's Ch's	O OX	O OX	
Pitch Bender		OX	OX	0-12 semitones
Control Change	0-95	OX	OX	
Program Change:	True #	OX 0-127 **************	OX 0-127 1-32	
System Exclusive		OX	OX	
System Common	:Song Pos :Song Sel :Tune	X X X	X X X	
System Real Time	:Clock :Commands	X X	X X	
Aux Messages	:Local ON/OFF :All Notes Off :Active Sense :Reset	X O 123 X X	O O 123-127 X X	
Notes				

Mode 1: OMNI ON, POLY   Mode 2: OMNI ON, MONO   O : Yes
Mode 3: OMNI OFF, POLY   Mode 4: OMNI OFF, MONO   X : No

General Comments

Different symbols, spellings, etc. may be used to represent the same information on different charts. The following comments will guide you through some of the the most common inconsistencies you may encounter when comparing charts from different sources.

- "O" and "X" symbols are used to indicate "Yes" and "No". The most common convention is to use "O" for "Yes". However, some charts use "X" for "Yes". Check the bottom right corner for a key to the symbols used.

- "OX" and " * " are often used to indicate a selectable function (one the user can enable/disable). However, selectability of a function may be mentioned in the Remarks or Notes areas, rather than indicated on the chart.

- Some items may be meaningless in the context of certain devices — for example, "Transmitted" information for a slave (receive-only) device. In such cases "N/A" (not applicable) may be used. Other charts may show an "X", "–" (dash), or simply leave the space blank.

- MIDI modes should be listed as follows: Mode 1 (OMNI ON, POLY), Mode 2 (OMNI ON, MONO), Mode 3 (OMNI OFF, POLY), and Mode 4 (OMNI ON POLY). The individual words "OMNI", "POLY", and "MONO" do not define any one of the four MIDI modes, but occasionally they are used for that purpose. Typically they are used to represent Modes 1, 3, and 4, but if you find these on a chart, you cannot be sure to which mode they refer. Check your owner's manual for more details.

- MIDI Mode messages may appear as OMNI ON, OMNI OFF, POLY ON, and MONO ON, or in the slightly abbreviated forms: OMNI ON/OFF, POLY, and MONO.

- Hexadecimal values are usually indicated with the suffix "$" or the prefix "H", or "h".

Header

- This area of the chart contains the manufacturer, model, and description of the device.

- Check the *Version* field on the chart and compare it to the version number of the piece of equipment you are using. If they are the same, the chart should accurately reflect the device's MIDI features. If the device's version number is higher, it may have features not documented on the chart. If the device's version number is lower, some of the features described on the chart may not be implemented on the device. If this is the case, check with the manufacturer to find out how to up-grade the device to the latest version.

Basic Channel

- *Default* : This field tells you what channel the device transmits on and/or recognizes when first turned on. If the default channel can be changed by the user, this will be indicated here. For example, an instrument whose default channel can be set to any channel would show "1-16" or "All Channels" here.

- *Changed* : This field indicates which MIDI channels can be assigned by the user during operation.

Mode

- *Default* : This indicates which of the four MIDI modes is active when the unit is first turned on. If the default mode can be changed, it will be indicated here.

- *Messages* : This field shows which of the four MIDI Mode messages are transmitted/recognized by the device. Be aware that some devices can be manually set to operate in different MIDI modes, even if they don't transmit or recognize mode messages.

- *Altered* : Only the *Recognized* column is valid for this entry. It is used to describe how a device will respond to a message requesting it to change to an invalid mode. For example, an instrument that does not operate in either of the two mono modes may treat the MONO message as an OMNI message in order to receive MIDI data. This will be indicated on the chart as: "MONO ON -> OMNI ON" or "MONO-> OMNI".

- Some instruments may alter modes based on the value of the second data byte of the MONO mode message. (See Part Three: Channel

Mode Messages for more details.) The value of this data is referred to as "M". Normally, this variable indicates how many mono channels a receiver should assign when it switches to a mono mode. Some devices that don't implement mono modes may switch to Mode 1 or Mode 3 depending on the value of M. This will be indicated on the chart with an expression such as: "MONO (M 1) –> Mode 1, (M=1) –> Mode 3".

Note Number

- *Transmitted* : The range of numbers given in this column show the actual MIDI note numbers transmitted by the device's keyboard (or other controller). The range 21-108 corresponds to the 88 keys of a grand piano. When the range is greater than the number of keys on the unit, it generally indicates a MIDI transpose feature of some kind. Check the chart's *Remarks* column for more details.

- *Recognized* : There are two ranges of note numbers that may be given in this column. The first indicates the range of note numbers recognized by the device. Note numbers outside of this range will be ignored (not played) by the device. (The maximum range of MIDI note numbers is 0-127.) The second range, labeled *True Pitch*, indicates the range of notes the device can play. It is unnecessary to show this unless the True Pitch range is less than the range of recognized note numbers. Recognized note numbers outside the True Pitch range are shifted in octaves until they fall within the range.

Velocity

- *Note On* : This will tell you if the unit transmits or recognizes variable attack velocity data. The maximum range of attack velocities is 1-127 (01-7FH). Some devices only transmit and/or recognize a subset of this range. Some drum machines, for example, transmit only two values, one for "normal" dynamics and another for "accents." In general, if the range is less than the full range the details will be shown here. For instance, "v = 40H Normal, v = 7FH Accent". If no range is given it is usually safe to assume that the the full range of velocities are transmitted and/or recognized.

- *Note Off* : This is similar to Note On except it shows whether or not a device transmits and/or recognizes Note Off release velocities. Many instruments transmit "Note On, v = 0" as an alternative to the implicit Note Off message. If this is the case, it is often indicated by showing the hex code for the Note On message in the Transmitted column — for example, "9nH v=0" or "$9n 00".

After Touch

- *Key's*: This indicates whether or not the device transmits/recognizes Polyphopnic Key Pressure messages (independent pressure values for each key).

- *Ch's*: This indicates whether or not the device transmits/recognizes Channel Pressure messages (one pressure value for the channel).

Pitch Bender

- Along with indicating whether or not the unit transmits/recognizes Pitch Wheel Change messages, the *Remarks* column will often give details on the resolution and range of the bender.

Control Change

- Many devices can transmit or recognize Registered Parameters and Non-Registered Parameters as well as General Purpose Controllers. This section of the chart will list which of these messages have been implemented, and to what parameters they are assigned. Be sure to read about these messages in *Part 3: Control Change Messages*.

- *Transmitted* :This column will list the controller ID numbers transmitted by the device's on board controllers. (See Part Three for a complete listing of all of the currently defined controller ID numbers.)

- *Recognized* :This column lists all of the recognized controller ID numbers and details which instrument parameters they can control.

Program Change

- *Transmitted* : The range of program numbers transmitted by the device is shown here. The maximum range is 0-127 (00-7FH).

- *Recognized* : The range of recognized program numbers is shown here. The actual numbers they correspond to on the particular unit are shown as the *True #* range.

System Exclusive

- From a software writer's point of view this can be the most significant aspect of an implementation. System Exclusive (SysEx) messages will give you access to the "private" sections of a device. In general, they allow you to send and receive memory dumps, and allow you to manipulate programming parameters which are not accessible via MIDI Channel messages.

There are also several Universal System Exclusive messages which a device may be able to transmit or recognize. Details about the formats of SysEx messages can be found in Part Three. Examples showing how to process these messages from within your own program are given in Part Four.

- The *Transmitted/Recognized* columns indicate whether or not System Exclusive messages are transmitted or recognized. The Remarks column should give details about message type and usage. The owner's manual should give details about the specific messages and their formats.

System Common

- This shows the unit's ability to transmit/recognize MTC Quarter-Frame, Song Position, Song Select, and Tune Request messages.

System Real-Time

- *Clock* : Transmission of the MIDI Clock message indicates that a device can be used as a master controller in a MIDI-synchronized system. Recognition of these messages means that the device can be "slaved" to an external source of MIDI Clock messages.

- *Messages* : The System Real-Time messages are: Stop, Start, and Continue. If these are transmitted/recognized by the unit, it will be indicated here along with a list of the particular messages utilized.

Aux Messages

- This section of the chart tells you how a device handles Local Control, All Notes Off, Active Sensing, and System Reset messages.

MIDI Hardware Profiles

One of the best ways to grasp the scope of potential MIDI applications is to examine the types of available MIDI hardware. In this section, we profile several types of MIDI hardware, giving a brief, general description of the capabilities of each type of device and a typical MIDI Implementation Chart for each device type. As you look over the charts, keep in mind that every item listed in the Transmitted column is a message that can be sent into a computer and manipulated by your own software; every item listed in the Recognized column represents a function or parameter which you can control remotely with your own software. The technical details of a MIDI implementation are explained in Part Three. Techniques to create applications that receive, process, and transmit all types of MIDI messages are demonstrated in Part Four.

Tone Modules

Also called MIDI slaves or expanders, tone modules contain sound-generating circuitry that produces sounds through synthesis or sampling technology. Tone modules generally do not have built-in performance controllers such as keyboard, wheels, etc., and are meant to be played remotely from a separate MIDI controller or from a sequencer. Most tone modules can be programmed from their front panel controls, but their ease of programming can usually be greatly enhanced with an editor (programming software).

A typical tone module will respond to most, if not all, MIDI performance-related messages (We'll go over these in detail in the next section.) You can write software to "play" the tone module with complete control of both the volume and pitch of the notes. Most tone modules can play from six to 16 or more notes simultaneously — all with the same sound. More sophisticated devices can produce different sounds simultaneously. The character of the sounds can be altered in real-time with effects such as pitch bend, vibrato, and tremolo.

MIDI Implementation Chart

Casio VZ-8M
Digital Synthesizer Tone Module

Version: 1.0

Function . . .		Transmitted	Recognized	Remarks
Basic	Default	1-16	1-16	Memorized
Channel	Changed	1-16	1-16	
	Default	Mode 3	Mode 3	
Mode	Messages	X	MONO, POLY	
	Altered	**************		
Note		X	0-127	
Number:	True Voice	**************	0-127	
Velocity	Note ON	X	O v = 1-127	
	Note OFF	X	X	
After	Key's	X	X	
Touch	Ch's	X	OX	
Pitch Bender		X	OX 0-48 semitones	14-bit resolution
	1	X	OX	Mod Wheel
	4	X	OX	Foot VR
	5	X	OX	Port. Time
	6,38	X	OX	Data Entry (RPN)
Control	7	X	OX	Master Volume
Change	10	X	OX	Pan
	12-31	X	OX	Def Control (*1)
	64	X	OX	Sustain
	65	X	OX	Port. On/Off
	100, 101	X	OX	RPN (*2)
Program		X	OX 0-63 or 0-127	
Change:	True #	**************		
System Exclusive		OX	OX	data dumps (etc.)
System	:Song Pos	X	X	
	:Song Sel	X	X	
Common	:Tune	X	X	
System	:Clock	X	X	
Real Time	:Commands	X	X	
Aux	:Local ON/OFF	X	O	
Messages	:All Notes Off	O	O	
	:Active Sense	X	X	
	:Reset	X	X	

Notes
  *1: one control change message transmitted as set in Total Control menu 0-5
  *2: RPN (Registered Parameter Number)
     #0: Pitch Bend Range
     Parameter values set using Data Entry

Performance Controllers

Also called master controllers, performance controllers contain no sound-generating hardware. They must be connected (via MIDI) to one or more tone modules to produce sound. The most common performance controllers are piano, or organ style, keyboards. However, there are performance controllers available for almost any kind of music expression. For example, there are guitar, wind (both trumpet and reed style), percussion, and violin controllers. There are even pitch-to-MIDI controllers, which can convert any monophonic (one note at a time) sound source into the appropriate MIDI messages to play melodies. Most performance controllers also provide an additional means for expressive performance, such as pitch wheels, foot pedals, and breath pressure.

MIDI Implementation Chart

Casio PG-380

Guitar Controller and Digital Synthesizer   Version: 1.0

Function . . .		Transmitted	Remarks
Basic	Default	1-16	Memorized
Channel	Changed	1-16	
	Default	Mode 3, 4 (M= 6)	
Mode	Messages	X	
	Altered	**************	
Note		36-91	can be shifted to
Number:	True Voice		24-79 or 48-103
Velocity	Note ON	O 9n v = 1-127	
	Note OFF	X 9n v = 0	
After	Key's	X	
Touch	Ch's	X	
Pitch Bender		O	14-bit resolution
	6,38	O	Data Entry (RPN)
	100, 101	O (RPN # 0)	RPN #0
Control Change			
Program		0-127	
Change:	True #	**************	
System Exclusive		OX	bend range
System	:Song Pos	X	
	:Song Sel	X	
Common	:Tune	X	
System	:Clock	X	
Real Time	:Commands	X	
Aux	:Local ON/OFF	X	
Messages	:All Notes Off	X	
	:Active Sense	X	
	:Reset	X	
Notes			

MIDI Implementation Chart

Yamaha WX 7
Wind Controller

Date: 4/7/1987
Version: 1.0

Function . . .		Transmitted	Remarks
Basic Channel	Default	1	Memorized
	Changed	1 & 2, 3 & 4	
Mode	Default	X	
	Messages	X	
	Altered	***************	
Note Number:		20-122	
	True Voice	***************	
Velocity	Note ON	O 9n v = 1-127	
	Note OFF	X 9n v = 0	
After Touch	Key's	X	
	Ch's	O	
Pitch Bender		O	7-bit resolution
Control Change	2	OX	Breath Contol
	7	OX	Volume
Program Change:		O 0-4	
	True #	***************	
System Exclusive		OX	bend range
System Common	:Song Pos	X	
	:Song Sel	X	
	:Tune	X	
System Real Time	:Clock	X	
	:Commands	X	
Aux Messages	:Local ON/OFF	X	
	:All Notes Off	X	
	:Active Sense	O	
	:Reset	X	
Notes			

Stand-Alone Instruments

A stand-alone MIDI instrument combines sound-generating circuitry and performance controllers in a single dedicated device. In terms of MIDI software, the two major sets of functions that you can access by computer are performance control and parameter programming.

MIDI Implementation Chart

Roland D-50
Digital Keyboard

Version: 1

Function . . .		Transmitted	Recognized	Remarks
Basic Channel	Default	1-16	1-16	
	Changed	1-16	1-16	Memorized
Mode	Default	Mode 3	Mode 1, 3, 4	
	Messages	POLY	MONO, POLY	
		OMNI OFF	OMNI ON/OFF	
	Altered	*************	Mode 2 → Mode 1	
Note Number:		12-108	0-127	
	True Voice	*************	12-108	
Velocity	Note ON	O	O v = 1-127	
	Note OFF	X 9n v = 0	X	
After Touch	Key's	X	X	
	Ch's	OX	OX	
Pitch Bender		OX	OX 0-12 semitones	9-bit resolution
Control Change	1	OX	OX	Modulation
	5	OX	OX	Port. Time
	7	OX	OX	Volume
	0-31	O	O (0, 2-4,8-31)	Ext. Control
	6,38	X	OX	Data Entry
	64	OX	OX	Hold 1
	65	OX	OX	Port. On/Off
	64-95	O	O (66-95)	Pedal Switch
	100,101	X	OX	RPN (#0, #1)
Program Change:		OX 0-127	OX 0-127	
	True #	*************	0-127	
System Exclusive		OX	OX	
System Common	:Song Pos	X	X	
	:Song Sel	X	X	
	:Tune	X	X	
System Real Time	:Clock	X	X	
	:Commands	X	X	
Aux Messages	:Local ON/OFF	X	O	Memorized
	:All Notes Off	O (123)	O (123-127)	
	:Active Sense	X	X	
	:Reset	X	X	
Notes	RPN # 0 : Pitch Bend Sensitivity RPN #1: Master Fine Tuning			

Sequencers

A hardware sequencer is a dedicated device that records and plays back performance-related MIDI messages. (With the right software, a computer can function as a sequencer too.) It is analogous in many ways to a multi-track tape recorder. In fact, the front panel controls often mimic a tape recorder's transport controls with buttons labeled, Start, Stop, Record, and Play. There is, however, one very important difference. A tape recorder records the actual sounds of a performance. A sequencer records the events in a performance (which keys, buttons and other controls are played). In terms of what it records, a sequencer has more in common with a player piano roll than it does with a tape recorder. A piano roll doesn't hold the sounds of the piano being played. It holds a record of the correct order in which particular keys where played. Unlike the piano roll, the sequencer's record is in the form of digital memory and can, therefore, be easily altered. This makes it possible to manipulate the original performance in many ways that would be difficult, or even impossible, with a tape recording.

A sequencer should provide at least one timing reference for synchronization with ATRs, MTRs, drum machines, and other sequencers. MIDI Clock and MIDI Time Code (MTC) can be used for direct synchronization with other MIDI sequencers and drum machines. Sync-to-tape can be used to synchronize with an ATR or VTR. SMPTE Time Code can be used to synchronize directly with LTC format SMPTE-controlled machines. Other synchronization schemes require some type of converter, such as MIDI Clock-to-SMPTE, or MTC-to-SMPTE. (See Part One: Synchronization Basics.)

MIDI Implementation Chart

Roland MC-500   Version: 1
MIDI Sequencer

Function . . .		Transmitted	Recognized	Remarks
Basic	Default	All	All	no basic channel
Channel	Changed	X	1-16 each	
	Default	Mode 3	X	
Mode	Messages	POLY	X	
		OMNI OFF		
	Altered	**************		
Note		0-127	0-127	
Number:	True Voice	**************		
Velocity	Note ON	O	O	
	Note OFF	X 9n v = 0	X	
After	Key's	O	OX	
Touch	Ch's	O	OX	
Pitch Bender		O	OX	
	0-63	O	OX	
	64-121	O	OX	
Control				
Change				
Program		O	OX 0-127	
Change:	True #	**************		
System Exclusive		OX	OX	
System	:Song Pos	OX	O sync = MIDI	
	:Song Sel	OX	O sync = MIDI	
Common	:Tune	O	O	
System	:Clock	OX	O sync = MIDI	
Real Time	:Commands	OX	O sync = MIDI	
Aux	:Local ON/OFF	O	O	
Messages	:All Notes Off	O (123)	O (123-127)	
	:Active Sense	X	X	
	:Reset	X	X	
Notes	When power is first applied, OMNI OFF and POLY are sent for all channels (1-16).			

Drum Machines

Also called rhythm programmers, drum machines are a specialized combination of sound-generating circuitry with a sequencer. The sounds on most currently available drum machines are short samples (digital audio recordings) of individual drum and percussion instruments. A drum machine is "pattern oriented." This makes it simple for a musician to create short, complex rhythm patterns and to link them together to create accompaniments for sequenced songs. Like sequencers, drum machines should provide at least one means of synchronization with ATRs, VTRs, sequencers, and other drum machines. MIDI Clock and FSK sync are the most common, but MIDI Time Code and LTC SMPTE Time Code are sometimes implemented.

MIDI Implementation Chart

Roland R-8
Rhythm Machine (Performance Section)

Date: 9/30/1988
Version: 1.0

Function . . .		Transmitted	Recognized	Remarks
Basic	Default	X	OFF	Memorized
Channel	Changed	X	OFF, 1-16	
Mode	Default	X	Mode 3	
	Messages	X	X	
	Altered	**************		
Note		X	0-127	
Number:	True Voice			
Velocity	Note ON	X	O 9n v = 1-127	n = section
	Note OFF	X	X	channel
After	Key's	X	X	
Touch	Ch's	X	X	
Pitch Bender		X	X	
Control Change	1	X	OX	Modulation
	10	X	OX	Pan
	16	X	OX	Gen. Purpose # 1
	17	X	OX	Gen. Purpose # 2
	18	X	OX	Gen. Purpose # 3
	19	X	OX	Gen. Purpose # 4
	80	X	OX	Gen. Purpose # 5
	81	X	OX	Gen. Purpose # 6
	82	X	OX	Gen. Purpose # 7
	83	X	OX	Gen. Purpose # 8
Program		X	X	
Change:	True #	**************		
System Exclusive		X	X	
System	:Song Pos	X	X	
	:Song Sel	X	X	
Common	:Tune	X	X	
System	:Clock	X	X	
Real Time	:Commands	X	X	
Aux	:Local ON/OFF	X	X	
Messages	:All Notes Off	X	X	
	:Active Sense	X	X	
	:Reset	X	X	
Notes	If channel is set to OFF, R-8 cannot recognize any messages.			

MIDI Implementation Chart

Roland R-8
Rhythm Machine (Instrument Section)

Date: 9/30/1988
Version: 1.0

Function . . .		Transmitted	Recognized	Remarks
Basic Channel	Default	1-16	1-16	Memorized
	Changed	1-16	1-16	
Mode	Default	Mode 3	Mode 3	
	Messages	X	X	
	Altered	**************		
Note Number:	True Voice	0-127 **************	0-127	assignable to each instrument (*1)
Velocity	Note ON	OX 9n v = 1-127	OX 9b v = 1-127	n = Inst Ch (*2)
	Note OFF	X 9n v = 0	X	b = Basic Ch
After Touch	Key's	X	X	
	Ch's	X	X	
Pitch Bender		X	X	
Control Change	1, 33	OX	OX	Modulation
	10	X	OX	Pan
	16, 48	OX	OX	Gen. Purpose # 1
	17, 49	OX	OX	Gen. Purpose # 2
	18, 50	OX	OX	Gen. Purpose # 3
	19, 51	OX	OX	Gen. Purpose # 4
	80	OX	OX	Gen. Purpose # 5
	81	OX	OX	Gen. Purpose # 6
	82	OX	OX	Gen. Purpose # 7
	83	OX	OX	Gen. Purpose # 8
Program Change:	True #	X **************	OX	
System Exclusive		O	OX	
System Common	:Song Pos	O	O sync = MIDI	
	:Song Sel	O	O sync = MIDI	0-9
	:Tune	X	X	
System Real Time	:Clock	O sync = Int/Tape	O sync = MIDI	
	:Commands	O sync = Int/Tape	O sync = MIDI	
Aux Messages	:Local ON/OFF	X	X	
	:All Notes Off	X	X	
	:Active Sense	O	X	
	:Reset	X	X	

Notes
*1: Can be changed manually and memorized.
*2: Transmit channek of each instrument can be changed manually from 1 to 16.

MIDI Workstations

A MIDI workstation is a stand-alone unit that combines the functions of a performance controller, tone module, sequencer, and drum machine into a single unit.

MIDI Implementation Chart

Korg M1
Music Workstation   Version: 1.0

Function . . .		Transmitted	Recognized	Remarks
Basic	Default	1-16	1-16	Memorized
Channel	Changed	1-16	1-16	
Mode	Default		Mode 3	
	Messages	X	X	
	Altered	**************		
Note		24-108	0-127	Seq. data is 0-127
Number:	True Voice	**************		in transmission
Velocity	Note ON	O 9n v = 1-127	OX 9n v = 1-127	Seq. data is 2-126
	Note OFF	X 9n v = 0	X	in transmission
After	Key's	X	X	
Touch	Ch's	OX	OX	
Pitch Bender		OX	OX	
Control Change	1	OX	OX	Pitch MG
	2	OX	OX	VDF Modulation
	6	OX	OX	Data Entry (MSB)
	7	OX	OX	Volume
	38	OX	OX	Data Entry (LSB)
	64	OX	OX	Sustain
	96	OX	OX	Data Increment
	97	OX	OX	Data Decrement
	100, 101	X	OX	RPN (#1)
	0-101	OX	OX	Send/Receive of Seq. data only
Program		OX 0-99	OX 0-127	
Change:	True #		0-99	
System Exclusive		OX	OX	data dumps (etc.)
System	:Song Pos	O	O	
	:Song Sel	O 0-19	O 0-19	
Common	:Tune	X	X	
System	:Clock	O clock = Int	O clock = Ext	
Real Time	:Commands	O clock = Int	O clock = Ext	
Aux	:Local ON/OFF	X	O	
Messages	:All Notes Off	X	O 123-127	
	:Active Sense	O	O	
	:Reset	X	X	
Notes				

Audio Effects

It is quite common to find MIDI ports on audio effects processors such as reverbs, delays, and flangers, as well as virtually all of the "multi-effects" processors on the market. The most basic implementations will allow MIDI Program Change messages to call up various preset effects from memory. More sophisticated implementations will allow the effect's parameters to be modified in real-time by various MIDI messages.

MIDI Implementation Chart

Lexicon LXP-5
Effects Processing Module   Version: 1.0

Function . . .		Transmitted	Recognized	Remarks
Basic	Default	1	1	
Channel	Changed	1-16	1-16	Memorized
Mode	Default Messages	X	Mode 3	
	Altered			
Note Number:	True Voice	X **************	0-127	used as controller
Velocity	Note ON	X	O v = 1-127	
	Note OFF	X	X	
After Touch	Key's	X	X	
	Ch's	X	O	
Pitch Bender		X	O	
Control Change	0-127	X	O	controllers can be patched to control effects parameters
Program Change:	True #	X **************	O 0-127	
System Exclusive		O	O	
System Common	:Song Pos	X	X	
	:Song Sel	X	X	
	:Tune	X	X	
System Real Time.	:Clock	X	O	used as controller
	:Commands	X	X	
Aux Messages	:Local ON/OFF	X	X	
	:All Notes Off	X	X	
	:Active Sense	X	X	
	:Reset	X	O	
Notes				

Mode 1: OMNI ON, POLY   Mode 2: OMNI ON, MONO   O : Yes
Mode 3: OMNI OFF, POLY   Mode 4: OMNI OFF, MONO   X : No

Audio Mixers

Implementing MIDI makes it possible to perform such sophisticated mixing features as, recalling "snap shots" of all mixing settings, real-time control of input levels, channel muting, EQ settings, etc. In fact, by using a MIDI sequencer to record and playback the messages sent to the mixer, it is possible to have completely automated mixing system.

MIDI Implementation Chart

Yamaha DMP 11   4/28/1988
Digital Mixing Processor   Version: 1.0

Function . . .		Transmitted	Recognized	Remarks
Basic Channel	Default	1-16	1-16	Memorized
	Changed	1-16	1-16	
Mode	Default	X	OMNI ON/OFF	Memorized
	Messages	X **************	X	
	Altered		X	
Note Number:	True Voice	X **************	0-127	
Velocity	Note ON	X	O v = 1-127	
	Note OFF	X	X	
After Touch	Key's	X	X	
	Ch's	X	X	
Pitch Bender		X	O 64 cent	7-bit resolution
Control Change	0-127	O	O	controllers can be assigned to control any parameter
Program Change:	True #	0-127 **************	O 0-127 0-96	
System Exclusive		O	O	bulk dump
System Common	:Song Pos	X	O	see notes
	:Song Sel	X	O	
	:Tune	X	X	
System Real Time	:Clock	X	O	see notes
	:Commands	X	O	
Aux Messages	:Local ON/OFF	X	X	
	:All Notes Off	X	X	
	:Active Sense	X	O	
	:Reset	X	O	
Notes	Song Pos, Song Sel, Clock and Clock Commands can be passed through MIDI Out.			

Part Three

MIDI Programmer's Reference

Part Three

MIDI Programmer's Reference

MIDI Hardware Summary

MIDI is a serial communications bus, similar to RS-232 or SCSI busses. Signals carried on the MIDI bus are used to control music-related peripherals. The MIDI signal is a serial voltage transmission, standardized at the rate of 31,250 bits per second. MIDI messages are made up of bytes encoded to define the type of message (status bytes), and bytes which carry data values relevant to the preceding status byte (data bytes).

The MIDI cable is a shielded, twisted pair cable, with a 5-pin DIN plug at either end. Pins 4 and 5 are connected to the twisted pair, and carry the MIDI signal. Pin 2 is grounded when attached to a MIDI port – the 5-pin DIN socket provided on MIDI devices to recevice the MIDI cable plug. (Pins 1 and 3 are currently unused but available for future expansion of the MIDI specification.)

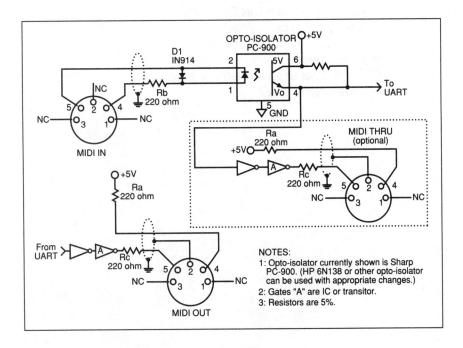

Transmission
- 31.25 k Baud
- Asynchronous
- Start bit/8 data bits/Stop bit

Circuit
- 5 mA current loop
- Logic 0 is current ON
- One output shall drive one input only
- Input opto-isolated
- Input requires less than 5 mA to turn on

Connectors
- DIN 5 pin, female, panel mount
- Pins 4 & 5 carry MIDI signal
- Pin 2 is ground (OUT and THRU)
- Pins 1 & 3 not used and left unconnected
- Labeled "MIDI IN" and MIDI OUT"

MIDI THRU
- Optional
- Direct copy of MIDI IN data
- Labeled "MIDI THRU"

Cables
- Maximum recommended length: 50 feet
- Ends terminate with DIN 5 pin, male
- DIN 5 pin, male cable plug
- Pins 4 & 5 carry MIDI signal
- Pin 2 is ground
- Pins 1 & 3 not used and left unconnected
- Shielded, twisted pair

In, Out, and Thru Ports

There are three types of MIDI ports: In, Out, and Thru. MIDI messages travel in only one direction through a MIDI cable, so a separate cable must be used for connections to each port. Each port is restricted to a single designated use. The MIDI In port allows a device to receive messages for its microprocessor. The MIDI Out port is used to transmit MIDI messages from the device's microprocessor to another device. The optional MIDI Thru port is used to pass an unaltered copy of the data stream to another device. There are only two valid port connections between two MIDI devices. The MIDI Out port of a transmitter may be connected to the MIDI In port of a receiver, or the MIDI Thru port of a receiver may be connected to the MIDI In port of an additional receiver.

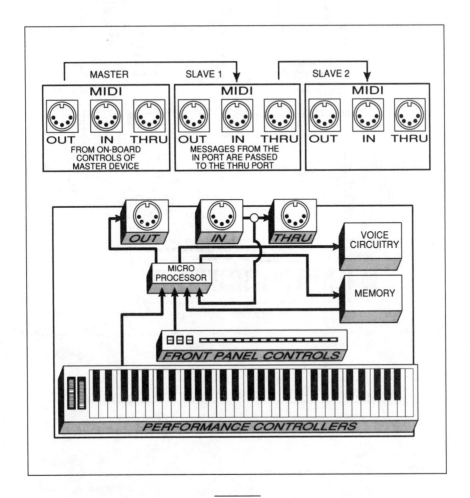

Typical Configurations

The MIDI ports provide not only a means for information exchange between linked devices, but also a means by which they can interactively control each other. The device transmitting MIDI data is said to be the master. Devices receiving MIDI data from the master are said to be slaves. A device with both MIDI In and Out ports can function as master or slave as needed. Multiple MIDI devices can be configured in a variety of useful ways using only their on-board MIDI In, Out and Thru ports.

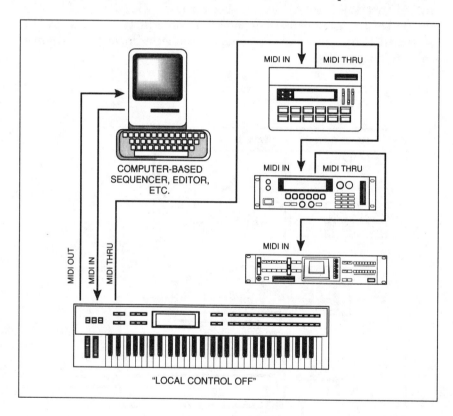

The previous illustration shows a MIDI sequencing system that includes a computer-based sequencer and a stand-alone synthesizer linked to a MIDI drum machine and two tone modules. Note that the stand-alone instrument is set to "Local Control Off", (See *Part 3: Local Control*.) This makes it possible to use the instrument as though it were a separate master controller and tone module. MIDI messages are sent from its controls to the computer/sequencer. The sequencer combines the incoming messages with MIDI Clocks and transmits them from its MIDI Out port to the MIDI In port of the synthesizer. (This allows the synthesizer to be played by the keyboard, or by previously recorded sequencer tracks.) The messages transmitted from the sequencer are routed to the drum machine and to additional tone modules via the synthesizer's MIDI Thru port. The configuration shown here allows the keyboard and sequencer to play any combination of instruments, as well as to synchronize the sequencer and drum machine.

A MIDI *switcher* is useful when you want to alternate control of a set of slaves between two or more master controllers. The configuration shown below makes it possible to switch control from a MIDI wind controller to a MIDI keyboard without disconnecting any MIDI cables.

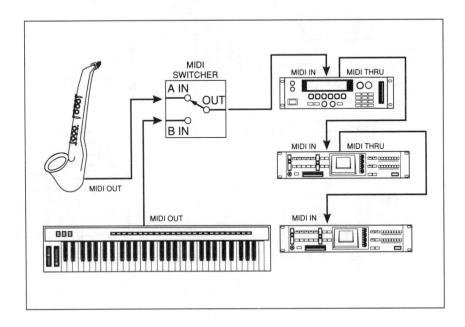

In a large MIDI system it is often necessary to reconfigure MIDI connections between various devices. A MIDI *patching matrix* is used to "rewire" the system without physically changing the connections. The configuration below shows a MIDI system consisting of seven devices. The MIDI In and Out ports of each device are connected to the patching matrix. The front panel controls of the patching matrix can be used to route messages from any MIDI Out port to any combination of MIDI In ports. A typical patching matrix can store a number of different configurations in memory. These can be recalled from the front panel, or via Program Change messages received on a designated MIDI In port.

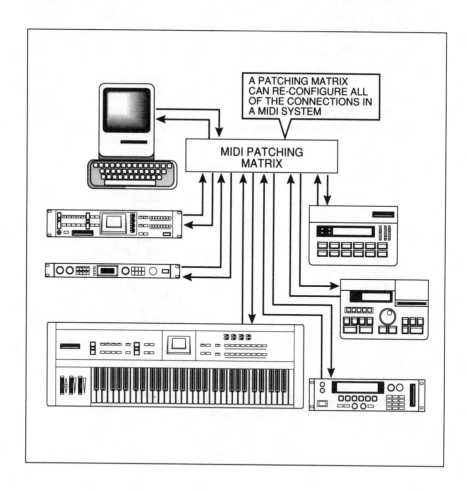

Bits and Bytes

The MIDI data stream consists of a series of bytes. As defined in the MIDI Specification, bytes can be one of two types, status bytes or data bytes. The bytes are ordered to form messages. Each message consists of a status byte, followed by zero or more data bytes. There are two general types of messages. Channel messages are used to address only those devices in a system assigned to a specific MIDI channel. System messages are used to address all devices in a system, regardless of their MIDI channel asssignment. The two general types are further divided into five subtypes — Channel Voice, Channel Mode, System Common, System Exclusive, and System Real-Time.

Byte Formats

Status Bytes

The most significant bit (bit 7) of a status byte is always set to 1.

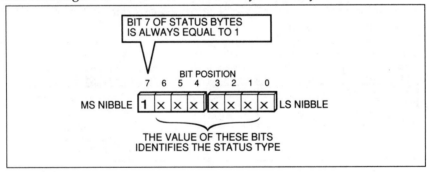

Data Bytes

The most significant bit (bit 7) of a data byte is always set to 0.

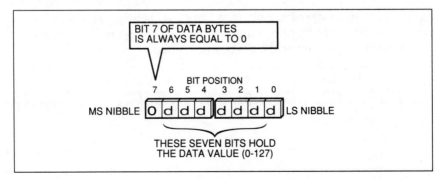

Message Formats

Channel Messages

The four low-order bits of all Channel message status bytes are used to specify the MIDI channel for the message. The four high-order bits are used to specify the particular message.

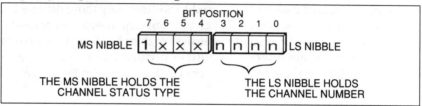

Channel Voice

There are seven Channel Voice messages. Each message can be tagged with one of 16 channel numbers. The range of values for Channel Voice status bytes is 128 - 239 (80H-EFH). Channel Voice messages have one or two data bytes following the status byte. The number of data bytes required is determined by the specific message.

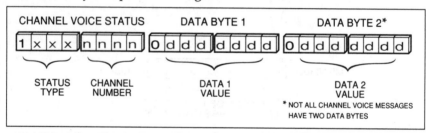

Channel Mode

Channel Mode messages are a special case of the three-byte Control Change message: status byte 176-191 (B0H-BFH). When the Control Change status byte is followed by a data byte greater than or equal to 121 (79H), the message is a Channel Mode message. Depending on the particular Channel Mode message, the third byte may or may not be ignored by the receiver. This byte, however, must always be transmitted.

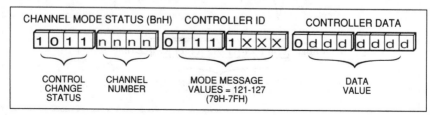

System Common Messages

System Common status bytes have values that range from 241 to 247 (F1H through F7H). System Common messages may have zero, one, or two data bytes. The number of data bytes is determined by the specific message.

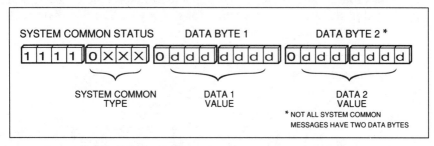

System Real-Time Messages

System Real-Time status bytes have values that range from 248-255 (F8H-FFH). System Real-Time messages have no data bytes.

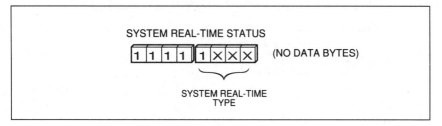

System Exclusive Messages

All System Exclusive messages must begin with the System Exclusive status byte (240, F0H) and end with the End Of Exclusive status byte (247, F7H), Any number of data bytes can be between these two bytes. The byte immediately following the SysEx status byte is the ID byte. The value of the ID byte specifies one of four types of System Exclusive messages, as shown in the following table.

ID Byte		SysEx Message Type
Hex	Decimal	
00-7CH	0-124	Manufacturer SysEx
7DH	125	Non-Commercial SysEx
7EH	126	Non-Real Time SysEx
7FH	127	Real Time SysEx

Manufacturer SysEx

If the value ID byte is between 0-124 (00-7CH), its value is a unique manufacturer ID number. Note that a value of zero indicates that the message holds the manufacturer ID in the next two bytes. Any number of bytes may follow the ID byte(s). The sizes and formats of these messages are published in the user documentation for the device. The final byte of the message must be an End Of Exclusive (EOX).

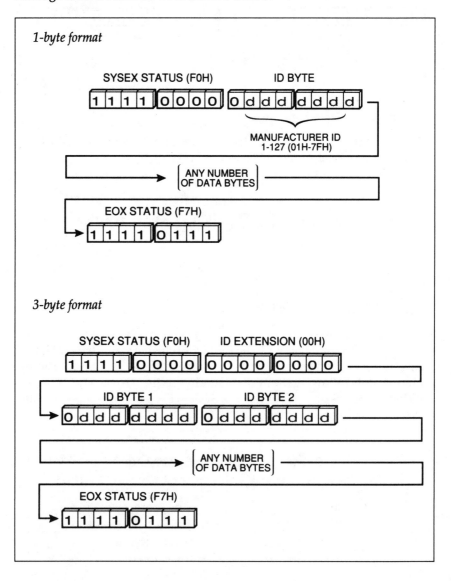

Universal Non-Real-Time SysEx

If the value of the ID byte is 126 (7EH), the message is a Universal Non-Real-Time message. With the exception of Sample Dump Standard messages, all Non-Real-Time messages have the same general format. The ID byte is followed by three additional bytes — device ID, sub ID #1, and sub ID #2. Any number of data bytes will follow these bytes, depending on the type of message specified by the two sub ID bytes. The final byte of the message must be an EOX. Sample Dump Standard messages have only one sub ID byte.

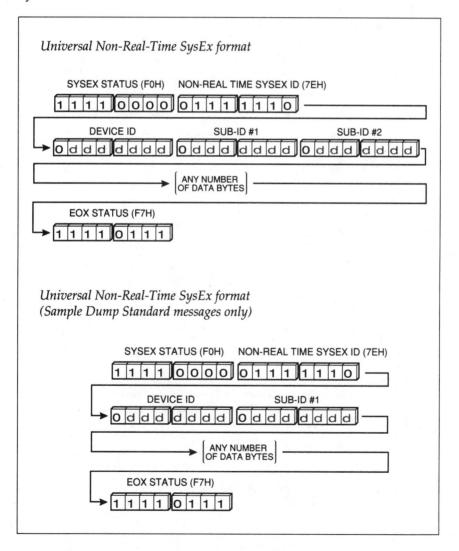

Universal Real Time SysEx

If the value of the ID byte is 127 (7FH), the message is a Universal Real-Time message. The format of these messages is the same as that of Non-Real-Time SysEx messages. The ID byte is followed by three additional bytes — device ID, sub ID #1, and sub ID #2. Depending on the type of message specified by the two sub ID bytes, any number of data bytes will follow. The final byte of the message must be an EOX.

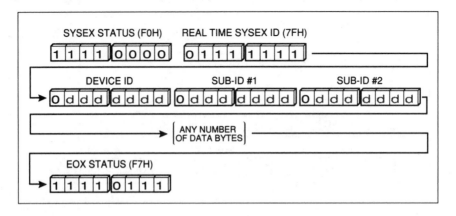

Universal Non-Commercial SysEx

If the value of the ID byte is 125 (7DH), the message is a Universal Non-Commercial message. This type of System Exclusive message was defined for research purposes and should never be generated from a commercial device. Any number of data bytes may follow the ID byte. The last byte of the message must be an End Of Exclusive status byte.

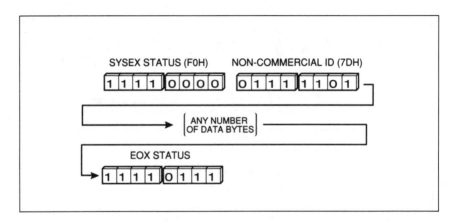

Channel Voice Messages

STATUS BYTE	HEX	DECIMAL	DATA BYTE 1	DATA BYTE 2
NOTE OFF	80-8F	128-143	NOTE NUMBER	RELEASE VELOCITY
NOTE ON	90-9F	144-159	NOTE NUMBER	ATTACK VELOCITY
POLY KEY PRESSURE	A0-AF	160-175	NOTE NUMBER	PRESSURE VALUE
CONTROL CHANGE	B0-BF	176-191	CONTROLLER ID	CONTROLLER VALUE
PROGRAM CHANGE	C0-CF	192-207	PROGRAM NUMBER	-
CHANNEL PRESSURE	D0-DF	208-223	PRESSURE VALUE	-
PITCH WHEEL CHANGE	E0-EF	224-239	PITCH BEND LSB	PITCH WHEEL MSB

Channel Voice messages are generated by manipulating the on-board performance controls of a MIDI instrument. For example, specific Channel Voice messages are transmitted by the instrument whenever you push a key, move the modulation wheel, or step on a foot switch. Instruments receiving Voice Channel messages will respond to them as though their own on-board controls are being manipulated. This makes it possible to control one MIDI device from another, or from a computer. (Remember that not all MIDI devices transmit or repond to every message defined in the MIDI specification. If a device receives a message that it doesn't recognize, it simply ignores it. The MIDI Implementation Chart included in the owner's manual of every MIDI device details which messages the device transmits and recognizes.)

A Channel Voice message Status byte identifies the specific message type and the MIDI channel used for its transmission. Following the Status byte are one or two data bytes. The number of data bytes, depending on the type of message. Following is a complete description of each of the Channel Voice messages.

Note On

Byte	Hex	Binary	Description
1	9n	1001 nnnn	status / channel number
2	kk	0kkk kkkk	note number
3	vv	0vvv vvvv	vv ≠ 00: attack velocity

Byte	Hex	Binary	Description
1	9n	1001 nnnn	status / channel number
2	kk	0kkk kkkk	note number
3	vv	0000 0000	vv = 00: Note Off

These messages are generated every time a key is pressed on a MIDI keyboard. This is how a note is turned on with MIDI. To stop a note once it has been turned on with a Note On message, it must be turned off with a Note Off message for the same note number. The Note On message contains the MIDI channel number in the lower four bits of its status byte. Sixteen separate MIDI channels (0-15) can be addressed. The note number value of byte 2 specifies any one of 128 discrete MIDI pitches. The receiving instrument is free to assign the note number to a specific pitch according to its own local tuning system(s). It is common practice to reference these values to standard equal tempered tuning, using note number 60 (3CH) as "middle C." If the keyboard is capable of transmitting dynamic information, the attack velocity value reflects how quickly the key is pushed down. The value representing the highest velocity is 127. The value representing the lowest velocity is 1. An attack velocity of zero is a special case. It is an alternative method for sending a Note Off message. (See *Running Status* for more details.)

If the keyboard is not capable of transmitting dynamic information, it is recommended that the value 64 (40H) be transmitted as attack velocity. As with the note number, the receiving instrument is free to interpret the velocity value. It is common practice to use higher velocity values for greater amounts of velocity-controlled effects — for instance, higher velocities can produce louder or brighter sounds. It is also common to allow the player to select from two or more velocity response curves.

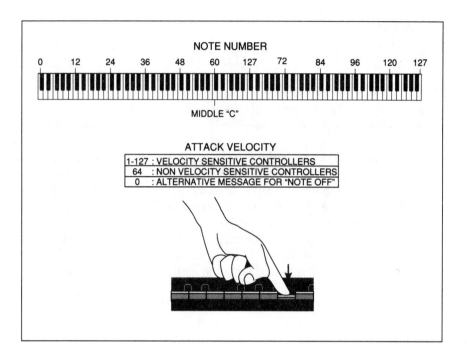

NOTE NUMBER

| 0 | 12 | 24 | 36 | 48 | 60 | 127 | 72 | 84 | 96 | 120 | 127 |

MIDDLE "C"

ATTACK VELOCITY

1-127	: VELOCITY SENSITIVE CONTROLLERS
64	: NON VELOCITY SENSITIVE CONTROLLERS
0	: ALTERNATIVE MESSAGE FOR "NOTE OFF"

Note Off

Byte	Hex	Binary	Description
1	8n	1000 nnnn	status / channel number
2	kk	0kkk kkkk	note number
3	vv	0vvv vvvv	release velocity

These messages are generated every time a key is released on a MIDI keyboard. Like the Note On message, the Note Off message contains the MIDI channel number (0-15), the note number (0-127), and a velocity value (0-127). If the keyboard is capable of transmitting dynamic information, the velocity value reflects how quickly the key released. The value representing the highest velocity is 127. The value representing the lowest velocity is 0. If the keyboard is not capable of transmitting dynamic information, it is recommended that the value 64 (40H) be transmitted as the release velocity.

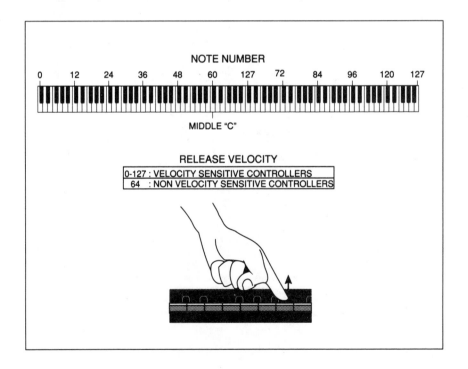

Polyphonic Key Pressure

Byte	Hex	Binary	Description
1	An	1010 nnnn	status / channel number
2	kk	0kkk kkkk	note number
3	vv	0vvv vvvv	pressure value

A keyboard with pressure sensitivity for each key will transmit these messages whenever the player applies extra pressure to the keys as they are held down. A separate message is generated for each key to which pressure is applied. This 3-byte message contains the MIDI channel number (0-15), the note number (0-127), and a pressure value (0-127) that corresponds to the amount of force applied to the key. The receiving instrument is free to respond to changes in pressure in any way the manufacturer chooses. The most common implementation is to provide the player with a set of selectable routing "destinations" for pressure changes, such as: vibrato rate and depth, loudness, pitch, and timbre control. Wherever a pressure change is routed, Polyphonic Key Pressure will produce independent changes for each voice.

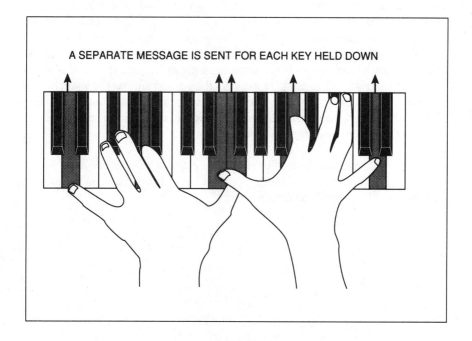

A SEPARATE MESSAGE IS SENT FOR EACH KEY HELD DOWN

Control Change

Byte	Hex	Binary		Description
1	Bn	1011	nnnn	status / channel number
2	cc	0ccc	cccc	controller ID number
3	vv	0vvv	vvvv	controller value

This message is used for real-time control of an instrument's performance functions (as opposed to its programming parameters). Control Change messages are generated whenever a MIDI controller (modulation wheel, foot pedal, foot switch, breath controller, etc.) is moved by the player. Each of the controllers of the transmitting instrument are assigned a controller ID value. Whenever any of the transmitter's controllers are moved, a message is sent, tagged with the appropriate controller ID number. The receiving instrument can use the message to control any parameter

As with all Voice Channel messages, the status byte contains the MIDI channel number in its lower four bits. The value of the second byte in the message identifies the specific controller. Note that, although the legal range of values for this byte is 0-127, the values 121-127 are reserved to specify Channel Mode messages. Therefore, a total of 121 MIDI controllers (0-120) is possible. The MIDI specification defines four categories of controllers — 14-bit, 7-bit, data increment/decrement, and parameter numbers. Controller ID numbers are generally assigned to musical instrument functions. (See the following table for details.) Manufacturers are free to use these controller numbers for other functions, as long as the messages are used in the defined format. However, they must notify the user (in the owner's manual) of any non-standard usage. Use Non-Registered Paramater Numbers rather than other controller ID numbers to control a large number of device specific functions.

The value of the third byte represents the current position of a particular controller within its overall range. A controller value of 0 means "no effect"; a value of 127 means "maximum effect."

Controller ID Numbers

14-Bit Controller MSBs

Controller Number		Description
Hex	**Decimal**	
00H	0	Undefined
01H	1	Modulation Controller
02H	2	Breath Controller
03H	3	Undefined
04H	4	Foot Controller
05H	5	Portamento Time
06H	6	Data Entry MSB
07H	7	Main Volume
08H	8	Balance Controller
09H	9	Undefined
0AH	10	Pan Controller
0BH	11	Expression Controller
0CH	12	Undefined
|	|	|
0FH	15	Undefined
10H	16	General Purpose Controller #1
11H	17	General Purpose Controller #2
12H	18	General Purpose Controller #3
13H	19	General Purpose Controller #4
14H	20	Undefined
|	|	|
1FH	31	Undefined

14-Bit Controller LSBs

Controller Number		Description
Hex	**Decimal**	
20H	32	LSB value for controller 0
21H	33	LSB value for controller 1
22H	34	LSB value for controller 2
|	|	|
3EH	62	LSB value for controller 30
3FH	63	LSB value for controllers 31

7-Bit Controllers

Controller Number		Description
Hex	**Decimal**	
40H	64	Damper Pedal (sustain)
41H	65	Portamento On/Off
42H	66	Sostenuto On/Off
43H	67	Soft Pedal
44H	68	Undefined
45H	69	Hold 2 On/Off
46H	70	Undefined
|	|	|
4FH	79	Undefined
50H	80	General Purpose Controller #5
51H	81	General Purpose Controller #6
52H	82	General Purpose Controller #7
53H	83	General Purpose Controller #8
54H	84	Undefined
|	|	|
5AH	90	Undefined
5BH	91	External Effects Depth
5CH	92	Tremolo Depth
5DH	93	Chorus Depth
5EH	94	Celeste (Detune) Depth
5FH	95	Phaser Depth

Parameter Value

Controller Number		Description
Hex	**Decimal**	
60H	96	Data Increment
61H	97	Data Decrement

Parameter Selection

Controller Number		Description
Hex	**Decimal**	
62H	98	Non-Registered Parameter Number LSB
63H	99	Non-Registered Parameter Number MSB
64H	100	Registered Parameter Number LSB
65H	101	Registered Parameter Number MSB

Undefined Controllers

Controller Number		Description
Hex	**Decimal**	
66H	102	Undefined
|	|	|
78H	120	Undefined

Reserved For Channel Mode Messages

Controller Number		Description
Hex	**Decimal**	
79H	121	Reset All Controllers
7AH	122	Local Control On/Off
7BH	123	All Notes Off
7CH	124	Omni Mode Off
7DH	125	Omni Mode On
7EH	126	Mono Mode On (Poly Mode Off)
7FH	127	Poly Mode On (Mono Mode Off)

Controller Positions as Data Values

As a continuous controller is moved from its minimum to its maximum postion, the controller's value should increment from 0 to its maximum value — 127 for 7-bit controllers, 16,383 for 14-bit controllers. The position of switch controllers is transmitted as 0 for "off" and 127 for "on." It is perfectly legitimate to use a continuous controller, such as a wheel, as a switch controller. An instrument receiving switch information must recognize the range 0-63 as "off" and 64-127 as "on".

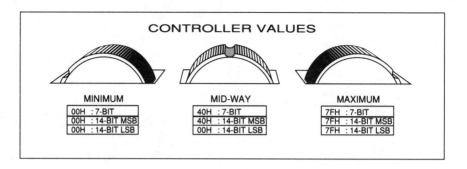

14-Bit Controllers

Controller ID numbers 0-31 correspond to the actual continuous controllers (sliders, wheels, pedals, etc.) of the transmitting device. Controller ID numbers 32-63 are reserved for sending an additional high-resolution value for controllers 0-31. Controller ID 32 corresponds to controller ID 0; controller ID 33 corresponds to controller ID 1, etc. This allows up to seven addtional bits to be added to a given controller's value, raising the resolution from 128 to 16,384 steps. Transmission of these high-resolution values is optional. High-resolution controllers should be implemented as follows:

The controller's value is sent as two complete Control Change messages. First, a message for the actual controller ID is sent. It contains the MSB (Most Significant Byte) of the high-resolution value. Then a message for the corresponding high-resolution controller ID is sent. It contains the LSB (Least Significant Byte) of the high-resolution value. Once both the MSB and LSB have been sent, it is not necessary to resend the MSB when only the LSB needs to be updated, such as when fine adjustments of the controller are made. The receiving instrument should reset its internal LSB value to 0 whenever it receives an MSB.

Controller Values		Amount of Effect
MSB	**LSB**	
00H	00H	minimum
40H	00H	mid-way
7FH	7FH	maximum

7-Bit Controllers

Controller ID numbers 64-95 are defined as 7-bit controllers. There is no optional method of sending an additional message with a high-resolution data byte for these controllers. Controllers 64-67 are defined as switch functions: hold pedal, portamento on/off, sustain, and soft pedal. Controllers 91-95 are defined as continuous functions for controlling the depth of the following audio effects: external effect, tremolo, chorus, detune, and phaser. Controllers 80-83 are defined as General Purpose Controllers (described below). Controllers 70-79 and 84-90 are currently undefined.

Balance, Pan, and Expression Controllers

The convention of having 0-127 represent increasing amounts of effect does not apply to the Balance, Pan, and Expression controllers. They are implemented as follows.

The Balance Controller (ID 8) is used to set the volume balance between two sound sources, such as left and right or lower and upper. A controller value of 0 corresponds to full volume for the left, or lower, source; 64 corresponds to equal volume; 127 corresponds to full volume for the upper, or right, source.

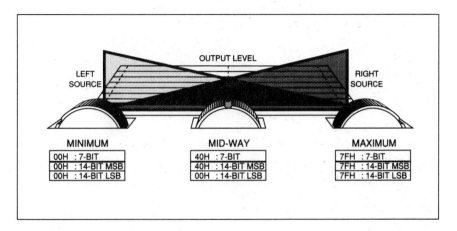

The Pan Controller (ID 10) is used to adjust the location of a single sound source in the stereo field. A controller value of 0 corresponds to hard left; 64 corresponds to center; 127 corresponds to hard right.

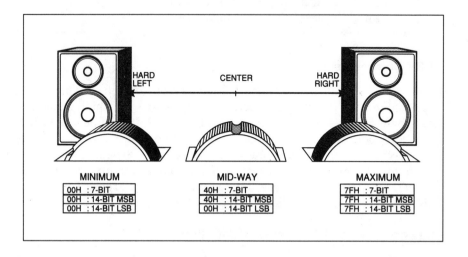

The Expression Controller (ID 11) is used to accent the programmed volume level. In other words, it can make a sound source louder, but not softer, than its current master volume setting. A controller value of 0 corresponds to the current master volume setting (no accent); 127 corresponds to the maximum loudness above the current volume setting (maximum accent).

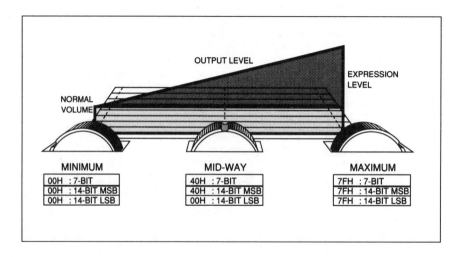

General Purpose Controllers

There are eight General Purpose Controllers defined by the MIDI specification. Controller ID numbers 16-19 are for 14-bit General Purpose Controllers 1-4; ID numbers 80-83 are for 7-bit General Purpose Controllers 5-8. General Purpose Controllers have no intrinsic functions assigned to them, and may be used to send and receive any sort of control information needed for a specific product.

Data Increment and Data Decrement

Byte	Hex	Binary	Description
1	Bn	1011 nnnn	status / channel number
2	60	0110 0000	Data Increment
3	7F	0111 1111	

Byte	Hex	Binary	Description
1	Bn	1011 nnnn	status / channel number
2	61	0110 0001	Data Decrement
3	7F	0111 1111	

Controller ID numbers 96 (60H) and 97 (61H) are defined as Data Increment and Data Decrement controllers. These controllers are used to send a generic "+1" or "-1" rather than an absolute value. The controller value byte for each of these messages should be set to 127, as shown.

Registered and Non-Registered Parameter Numbers

RPN Number		Description
LSB	**MSB**	
00H	00H	`Pitch Bend Sensitivity`
01H	00H	`Fine  Tuning`
02H	00H	`Coarse  Tuning`

Registered and Non-Registered Parameter Numbers can be used to control any sound or performance parameter of an instrument. There are currently three Registered Parameter Numbers (RPNs) defined: Pitch Bend Sensitivity (RPN 0), Fine Tuning (RPN 1), and Coarse Tuning (RPN 2). Non-Registered Parameter Numbers may be assigned by the manufacturer as needed. The following guidelines are recommended for implementing these controllers.

- Manufacturers may assign any parameter to any Non-Registered Parameter Number. A list of assignments should be published in the device's owner's manual.

- The values of Registered or Non-Registered Parameters are altered by Data Entry MSB , Data Entry LSB, Data Increment, or Data Decrement Control Change messages as follows:

  1. Transmit the Registered or Non-Registered Parameter Number corresponding to the parameter to be accessed.

  2. Transmit the desired Data Entry, Data Increment, or Data Decrement value for the parameter.

- As Registered Parameter Numbers are standardized, recognition of them may be enabled on power-up. All other rules for their use are the same as those for Non-Registered Parameters.

- In order to avoid confusion between different devices, reception of Non-Registered Parameter Numbers should be disabled on power-up. This convention allows these numbers to be transmitted safely at any time.

- Once the reception of Non-Registered and/or Registered Parameter Numbers has been enabled, the receiver should wait until it receives both an MSB and an LSB for a parameter number, to verify that it is operating on the correct parameter.

- The transmitter may send only an LSB or only an MSB to change the parameter number, and the receiver should be able to respond accordingly. The transmitter has no idea when the reception was enabled on the receiver, and the receiver is waiting initially for both the LSB and the MSB. Therefore, it is suggested that the transmitter send out the LSB and MSB each time a new parameter number is selected.

- Once a new Parameter Number is chosen, it retains its old value until a new Data Entry, Data Increment, or Data Decrement value is received.

Pitch Bend Sensitivity

Pitch Bend Sensitivity is defined as RPN 0 (00 00H). The Data Entry MSB value corresponds to the sensitivity in semitones. The LSB corresponds to the sensitivity in units of 1/128 of a semitone.

Fine Tuning

Fine Tuning is defined as RPN 1 (00 01H). The Data Entry MSB value corresponds to pitch displacement in units of 1/64 of one semitone. The LSB further subdivides each MSB unit into 128 steps. This provides an overall fine tuning range of ±1 semitone, with a resolution that divides a semitone into 8,192 steps. The following table details the implementation.

Resolution: 100/8192 cents per bit
Range: 100/8192 * (-8192) to 100/8192 * (+8192)

Data Entry Value		Displacement in cents
MSB	LSB	
00H	00H	100/8192 * (-8192)
40H	00H	100/8192 * (0)
7FH	7FH	100/8192 * (+8191)

Coarse Tuning

CoarseTuning is defined as RPN 2 (00 02H). The Data Entry MSB value corresponds to pitch displacement in units of one semitone. This provides an overall coarse tuning range of 64 semitones below to 63 semitones above the original pitch, with a resolution of one semitone per step. The LSB Data Entry value is not used. The following table details the implementation.

Resolution: 100cents per bit
Range: 100 * (-64) to 100 * (+64)

Data Entry Value	Displacement in cents
MSB	
00H	100 * (-64)
40H	100 * (0)
7FH	100 * (+64)

Mode 4 Global Controllers

When a receiving instrument is in MIDI Mode 4 (and able to receive on more than one channel) a Global Controller can be used to affect all voices, regardless of their channel assignments. This is accomplished by transmitting any controller(s) intended to affect all voices on the channel number one step below the receiver's basic channel. For example, if the receiver's basic channel is set to 16, then Global Controller messages are sent on channel 15. If the receiver's basic channel is set to 1, then the Global Controller messages are sent on channel 16. Recognition of Global Controller messages is optional for the receiver.

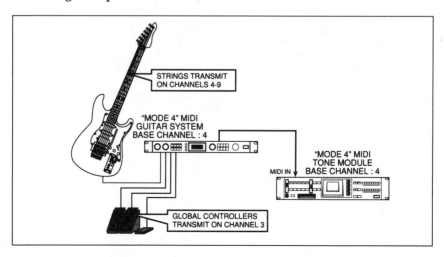

STRINGS TRANSMIT ON CHANNELS 4-9

"MODE 4" MIDI GUITAR SYSTEM BASE CHANNEL : 4

"MODE 4" MIDI TONE MODULE BASE CHANNEL : 4
MIDI IN

GLOBAL CONTROLLERS TRANSMIT ON CHANNEL 3

Program Change

Byte	Hex	Binary		Description
1	Cn	1100	nnnn	status / channel number
2	pp	0ppp	pppp	program ID number

This message is used to change the active program number when changing presets on a MIDI device. The program number is a reference to a preset sound of a musical instrument, but it may also be used to reference other types of presets as well. For example, program numbers can reference a preset effect of an audio processor, the rhythm patterns of a drum machine, or the keyboard "setups" of a master controller. The status byte of the message contains the MIDI channel number (0-15), the data byte contains the ID number of the selected program (0-127). On many instruments, the tranmission/reception of these messages can be selectively enabled or disabled by the player.

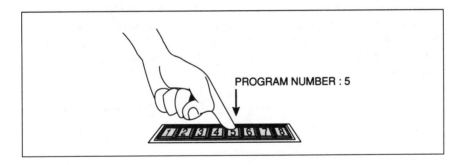

PROGRAM NUMBER : 5

Channel Pressure

Byte	Hex	Binary	Description
1	Dn	1101 nnnn	status / channel number
2	vv	0vvv vvvv	pressure value

A keyboard that is pressure-sensitive will transmit these messages whenever the player applies extra force to any of the keys as they are held down (This is often referred to as After Touch.) MIDI wind instruments commonly transmit breath pressure as Channel Pressure messages. Unlike Polyphonic Key Pressure, a single message is generated, regardless of the number of keys held down. The Channel Pressure value is applied to all of the voices assigned to its channel number. The status byte contains the MIDI channel number (0-15). The data byte contains the pressure value. This value corresponds to the sum of the amount of pressure applied to all keys (0 is no pressure; 127 is maximum pressure.) The receiving instrument is free to respond to changes in pressure in any way the manufacturer chooses. The most common implementation is to provide the player with a set of selectable routing "destinations" for pressure changes, such as: vibrato rate and depth, loudness, pitch, and timbre control. Wherever it is routed, Channel Pressure will produce global changes for all voices on the same channel.

ONE MESSAGE IS SENT ALL NOTES ON THE MIDI CHANNEL

Pitch Bend Change

Byte	Hex	Binary	Description
1 En	1111 nnnn	status / channel number	
2 ll	0111 1111	pitch bend LSB	
3 hh	0hhh hhhh	pitch bend MSB	

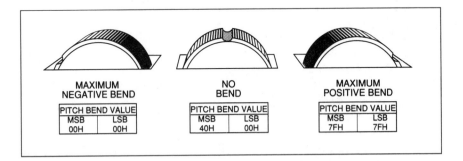

MAXIMUM NEGATIVE BEND		NO BEND		MAXIMUM POSITIVE BEND	
PITCH BEND VALUE		PITCH BEND VALUE		PITCH BEND VALUE	
MSB	LSB	MSB	LSB	MSB	LSB
00H	00H	40H	00H	7FH	7FH

This message is transmitted whenever the intrument's pitch bender (usually a wheel) is moved. Virtually every pitch bender is implemented as a bidirectional controller and can produce positive or negative pitch displacement from the "normal" (no bend) position.

The status byte of the message contains the MIDI channel number (0-15). The first data byte holds the LSB position value. The second data byte holds the MSB position value. This makes it possible to produce pitch bend effects with up to 14 bits of resolution. It is not necessary to use all 14 bits, but we are so sensitive to changes in pitch that 7-bit resolution pitch bends can sound coarse. Many manufacturers use eight or more bits of bender resolution. Both data bytes must always be sent, even if only 7-bit resolution is used. The following table details the implemention.

Pitch Bend Value		Pitch Displacement
MSB	LSB	
00H	00H	maximum negative bend
40H	00H	no bend
7FH	7FH	maximum positive bend

Channel Mode Messages

STATUS BYTE	HEX	DECIMAL
CONTROL CHANGE	B0-BF	176-191

DATA BYTE 1	HEX	DECIMAL	DATA BYTE 2
RESET ALL CONTROLLERS	79	121	IGNORED
LOCAL CONTROL	7A	122	ON / OFF
ALL NOTES OFF	7B	123	IGNORED
OMNI MODE OFF	7B	124	IGNORED
OMNI MODE ON	7C	125	IGNORED
MONO MODE ON	7D	126	NUMBER OF CHANNELS
POLY MODE ON	7F	127	IGNORED

Channel Mode messages determine whether an instrument will respond to all channels or to only a selected one. These messages also determine whether an instrument will assign incoming Channel Voice messages to its internal voices *polyphonically* (more than one note per MIDI channel) or *monophonically* (one note per MIDI channel). Regardless of its current mode, a receiver should only respond to Channel Mode messages that are on its assigned basic channel. It should ignore Mode messages on any other channel. Channel Mode messages use the same status byte as the Control Change message. The value of the second byte of the message determines whether it should be interpreted as a "normal" Control Change or message or as a Channel Mode message. Values of 121 or greater are Channel Mode messages.

Reset All Controllers

Byte	Hex	Binary	Description
1	Bn	1011 nnnn	status / channel number
2	79	0111 1001	Reset All Controllers
3	00	0000 0000	ignored

This message is used to reset all the controllers of a receiver to their initialized states. This includes *all* controllers — pitch bend, mod wheel, polyphonic key pressure, channel key pressure, and any other switch or continuous controller. An instrument receiving this message will respond according to its current MIDI mode, as shown in the following table.

MIDI Mode	Response to Reset All Controllers Message
Mode 1	ignore message
Mode 2	ignore message
Mode 3	reset controllers on basic channel only
Mode 4	reset controllers on same channel as message only

Local Control

Byte	Hex	Binary		Description
1	Bn	1011	nnnn	status / channel number
2	7A	0111	1010	Local Control
3	00	0000	0000	Off

Byte	Hex	Binary		Description
1	Bn	1011	nnnn	status / channel number
2	7A	0111	1010	Local Control
3	7F	0111	1111	On

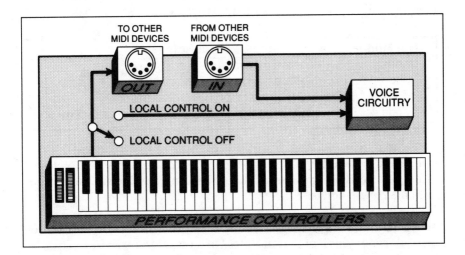

This message is used to disconnect an instrument's built-in keyboard from its internal sound-generating hardware. It is common practice to disconnect any built-in controllers as well as the program select switches. When in Local Control Off, the keyboard and other controllers continue to send data to the MIDI Out port, while the internal sound generators will respond only to data arriving at the MIDI In port. Local Control On reconnects the keyboard and controllers to the internal sound generators.

All Notes Off

Byte	Hex	Binary		Description
1	Bn	1011	nnnn	status / channel number
2	7B	0111	1011	All Notes Off
3	00	0000	0000	ingored

This message is used to turn off all notes that have previously been turned on by Note On messages received from the MIDI In port. Receiving instruments aren't required to recognize this message. Since receivers may not recognize the All Notes Off message, it should never be sent instead of individual Note Off messages. The All Notes Off message should only be sent in a "panic" situation, such as pressing the Stop button on a sequencer. A MIDI instrument should be able to distinguish between notes turned on by its built-in keyboard and notes turned on via MIDI. Only those notes turned on via MIDI should be turned off by the All Notes Off message. If the instrument can't distinguish between its own keyboard and incoming MIDI data, it must ignore the All Notes Off message. An instrument receiving this message will respond according to its MIDI mode as shown below.

MIDI Mode	Response to All Notes Off
Mode 1	ignore message
Mode 2	ignore message
Mode 3	turn off notes on basic channel only
Mode 4	turn off notes on same channel as message only

If the Hold switch, controller ID 64 (40H), is "on" when an All Notes Off message is received, the message should be recognized, but not acted upon, until the Hold swith is "off."

The four MIDI Mode messages: Omni On, Omni Off, Mono On, and Poly Off are also "synonyms" for the All Notes Off message. A receiving instrument that recognizes the All Notes Off message should respond to these four messages in the same way as well as responding appropriately to the Mode message.

Omni Off

Byte	Hex	Binary	Description
1	Bn	1011 nnnn	status / channel number
2	7C	0111 1100	Omni Mode Off
3	00	0000 0000	ignored

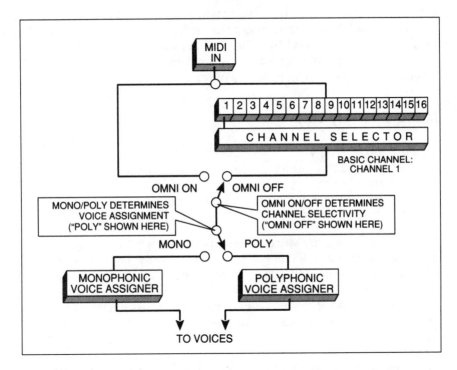

When set to Omni Off, the instrument can be assigned to a specific MIDI channel. It will respond only to messages on the assigned channel(s), ignoring messages on any other channel, and it will transmit voice messages only on the assigned channel(s). It is common practice to assign both receive and transmit channels to the same number, but an instrument may, in fact, transmit and receive on different channels.

Omni On

Byte	Hex	Binary	Description
1	Bn	1011 nnnn	status / channel number
2	7D	0111 1101	Omni Mode On
3	00	0000 0000	ignored

When set to OMNI On, an instrument will try to respond to all messages it receives (via MIDI In) without regard to channel number. All messages the instrument transmits (via MIDI Out) will be assigned to one channel. Any instrument not capable of channel assignment must be set to channel 1, otherwise, assignment can be to any of the 16 MIDI channels.

Mono On (Poly Off)

Byte	Hex	Binary	Description
1	Bn	1011 nnnn	status / channel number
2	7E	0111 1110	Mono Mode On
3	mm	000m mmmm	number of mono channels

When set to Omni Off/Mono, an instrument assigns incoming Channel Voice messages to its internal voices monophonically. The instrument will play only one note per MIDI channel, but it may play more than one mono channel at a time. The number of MIDI channels is determined by the value M in the last byte of the message. Channels are assigned sequentially, starting with the receiver's basic channel, according to the following calculation.

Channels n through (n + M) - 1 are assigned where n equals the basic channel (1-16), and M equals the number of mono channels (1-16).

M=0 is a special case. The instrument should assign voices, one per channel, from its basic channels n-16, until all available voices are used. For example, a MIDI guitar controller that transmits notes for each of its strings on a separate channel would assign notes to six mono channels. Its M value would be 6. If its basic channel were set to 3, it would transmit on channels 3-8. If its basic channel were set to 11, it would transmit on channels 11-16.

When set to Omni On/Mono, an instrument assigns all incoming Channel Voice messages to a single internal voice. The instrument will respond to all incoming messages on any channel, but will never play more than one voice at a time. If the M value of the Mono message is greater than 1, it will be ignored.

Poly On (Mono Off)

Byte	Hex	Binary	Description
1	Bn	1011 nnnn	status / channel number
2	7F	0111 1111	Poly Mode On
3	00	0000 0000	ignored

When set to Poly, the instrument assigns incoming Channel Voice messages to its internal voices polyphonically. This makes it possible to transmit and receive more than one note at a time (chords) on a single MIDI channel.

System Common Messages

System Common messages, because they are intended for all devices in a MIDI system, are not tagged with a channel number in the status byte.

STATUS BYTE	HEX	DECIMAL	DATA BYTE 1	DATA BYTE 2
MTC QUARTER FRAME	F1	241	MESSAGE TYPE	-
SONG POSITION POINTER	F2	242	SONG POSITION LSB	SONG POSITION MSB
SONG SELECT	F3	243	SONG ID NUMBER	-
UNDEFINED	F4	244	-	-
UNDEFINED	F5	245	-	-
TUNE REQUEST	F6	246	-	-
END OF EXCLUSIVE	F7	247	-	-

MTC Quarter-Frame

Byte	Hex	Binary	Description
1	F1	1111 0001	Status
2	nd	0nnn dddd	message number/data

This message is used by instruments that transmit or recognize MIDI Time Code (MTC). These messages are only sent when time code is running, such as when an ATR or VTR is in play mode. Quarter-Frame messages are not sent during fast forward, rewind, or shuttle modes. (The MTC Full Message is used to cue up the receiver before going back to the play mode.) There are eight variations of the message. Each acts a timing pulse for the system, and also carries four of the 32 bits needed to specify a unique location in SMPTE time code. The reception of a complete sequence of eight Quarter-Frame messages is required to completely define the SMPTE time — two each for hours, minutes, seconds, and frames. Therefore, MTC can only update SMPTE time once every two frames. A device can provide higher resolution by interpolating the time between the arrival of Quarter-Frame messages. Since these messages are sent at the rate of 4/frame, it will take from 2-4 SMPTE frames to lock synchronization between SMPTE and MTC devices.

Quarter Frame Message Order

Message Number	SMPTE Data
0	frame number LS nibble
1	frame number MS nibble
2	seconds count LS nibble
3	seconds count MS nibble
4	minutes count LS nibble
5	minutes count MS nibble
6	hours count LS nibble
7	hours count MS nibble and time code type

The data byte contains a message number (0-7) and four bits of data for one of the four SMPTE time fields. The sequence must always be transmitted in serial order (either forward or reverse). The messages are sent at time intervals corresponding to a Quarter-Frame of SMPTE time. For example, at 30 frames per second, Quarter-Frame messages will be sent at a rate of 120 per second. This corresponds approximately to one message every 8.3 milliseconds. At 30 frames per second, with time code running in the forward direction, the messages would be sent in the sequence shown below. (If time code were running in reverse, the sequence would be reversed.)

```
F1 0d frame LS
( 8.3 ms)
F1 1d frame MS
( 8.3 ms)
F1 2d seconds LS
( 8.3 ms)
F1 3d seconds LS
( 8.3 ms)
F1 4d minutes LS
( 8.3 ms)
F1 5d minutes MS
( 8.3 ms)
F1 6d hours LS
( 8.3 ms)
F1 7d hours MS / time code type
```

The eight messages are sent repeatedly as long as time code is running. The messages F1 0d and F1 4d are always sent on the frame boundaries of the running time code. The illustration on the following page shows the timing of transmission of these messages relative to SMPTE time.

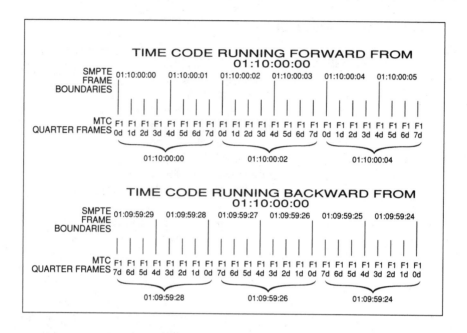

Quarter-Frame Data Format

Two Quarter-Frame messages are needed to transmit the data for each SMPTE time field. Since it takes eight messages to transmit complete SMPTE data, SMPTE time is updated every two frames. Each message carries a 4-bit nibble of data. The formats for the completed fields are shown below.

Frame Count: MSN   LSN
                    xxxy   yyyy

xxx   These three bits are undefined and reserved for future use. They should be ignored by the receiver and set to 0 by the transmitter.

yyyy   Frame number (0-29)

Seconds Count: MSN   LSN
                    xxxy   yyyy

xx   These two bits are undefined and reserved for future use. They should be ignored by the receiver, and set to 0 by the transmitter.

yyyyy Seconds count (0-59)

Minutes Count: MSN LSN
                 xxxy yyyy

xx   These two bits are undefined and reserved for future use. They
        should be ignored by the receiver, and set to 0 by the transmitter.

yyyyy Minutes count (0-59)

Hours Count: MSN LSN
               xyyz zzzz

x   This bit is undefined and reserved for future use. It should be
        ignored by the receiver, and set to 0 by the transmitter.

yy   Time code type:

                0 = 24 frames/second
                1 = 25 frames/second
                2 = 30 frames/second (drop frame)
                3= 30 frames/second (non-drop)

zzzzz Hours count (0-23)

The following table shows SMPTE time with the hex values as they would
be assembled after the reception of the eight Quarter-Frame messages
required to carry the data. Following the table are the hex values as they
would be transmitted via Quarter-Frame messages.

SMPTE Type	Hours	Minutes	Seconds	Frames
3	02	45	15	13
6xH	02H	2DH	0FH	0DH
(bits 5 & 6 are set)*				

* The values for SMPTE type (6xH) and hours (02H) are summed (62H)


```
F1 0D frame LS
F1 10 frame MS
F1 2F seconds LS
F1 30 seconds LS
F1 4D minutes LS
F1 52 minutes MS
F1 62 hours LS
F1 76 hours MS / time code type
```

Song Position Pointer

Byte	Hex	Binary	Description
1	F2	1111 0010	Status
2	ll	0lll llll	song position LSB
3	hh	0hhh hhhh	song position MSB

This message is used to indicate a location within a MIDI sequence. The Song Position Pointer (SPP) is 0 at the start of a sequence and is incremented by one for every six ticks of the MIDI clock. The MIDI specification defines the MIDI clock rate as 24 ticks per quarter-note, so the SPP is the number of 16th notes from the start of the sequence. The Song Position Pointer message should be ignored if the receiver is not set to recognize MIDI Start, Stop, and Continue messages.

The receiver must perform the following calculation to convert the SPP to a corresponding location in its internal sequence.

$$\text{SPP} * (6 * \text{time base}) = \text{internal location}$$

The time base is equal to the number of internal ticks per MIDI tick. For example, the internal clock of a sequencer with a resolution of 96 ticks per quarter-note has four ticks for every MIDI clock tick. Its time base is equal to 4. The following table shows the location of an SPP value of 10 for four common sequencer time bases.

Time Base	Internal Location (SPP=10)	Internal Resolution
1	60 ticks	24/quarter-note
2	120 ticks	48/quarter-note
4	240 ticks	96/quarter-note
8	480 ticks	192/quarter-note
16	960 ticks	384/quarter-note

In general, it is good practice to transmit SPPs only when the system is stopped, as opposed to "on the fly." The reason for this, is that most devices will need a certain amount of time (as much as several seconds) to advance their internal pointer to the new song position and be ready to play. It is the responsibility of the receiver to keep track of an incoming Continue message, as well as any subsequent timing clocks that may arrive, while it is in the process of updating to a new song position. In such cases the receiver should begin incrementing its internal song position, starting at the new SPP value, and "drop in" after it has caught up with the running Timing Clocks.

Song Select

Byte	Hex	Binary	Description
1	F3	1111 0011	Status
2	ss	0sss ssss	song ID number

This message is used to select a specific "song" from a sequencer or drum machine. The song ID number specifies the sequence that will begin playing when the receiver gets a Start message. Song Select should be ignored if the receiver is not set to recognize MIDI Start, Stop, and Continue messages.

Tune Request

Byte	Hex	Binary	Description
1	F6	1111 0110	Status

When an instrument receives this message, it will perform its on-board tuning routine (if it has one).

End Of Exclusive

Byte	Hex	Binary	Description
1	F7	1111 0111	Status

This message is sent to indicate the end of a System Exclusive message. Even though receipt of any status byte (except for System Real Time status bytes) will terminate a System Exclusive message, the End Of Exclusive message should always be sent as the last byte in a SysEx transmission.

System Real-Time Messages

STATUS BYTE	HEX	DECIMAL
TIMING CLOCK	F8	248
UNDEFINED	F9	249
START	FA	250
CONTINUE	FB	251
STOP	FC	252
UNDEFINED	FD	253
ACTIVE SENSING	FE	254
SYSTEM RESET	FF	255

Like System Common messages, System Real-Time messages are intended for all devices in a MIDI system and are, therefore, not tagged with channel numbers. With the exception of the Active Sensing and System Reset messages, System Real-Time messages are used in connection with the synchronization of devices such as sequencers and drum machines. Not all devices need to recognize Real-Time Messages but, even when they are ignored, they require some processing. These messages may appear anywhere within a series of MIDI bytes. For example, they could appear between the bytes of a Note On or Control Change message. In such cases the receiver must not interpret the Real-Time message as a new status. For the same reason, reception of Real-Time messages should not affect or interrupt the receiver's Running Status buffer. (See *Running Status* and *Parsing MIDI Data*.)

The fact that System Real-Time messages can be inserted anywhere in the MIDI data stream makes it possible to maintain accurate synchronization between devices while other tasks (such as turning notes on and off) are in progress. It is common practice for clock-based devices to merge incoming Timing Clock (as well as Stop, Start, and Continue) messages with the MIDI data stream they transmit. This allows additional devices to maintain synchronization with the transmitter of the Timing Clock messages. System Real-Time messages are given priority when the two data streams are merged . The actual order of bytes may be changed when there is a conflict. For example, a Note On status byte might be delayed slightly to accomodate a Timing Clock. System Real-Time messages must always be sent in the same order that they were received. As noted previously, System-Real Time messages may also be inserted between the bytes of any other messages.

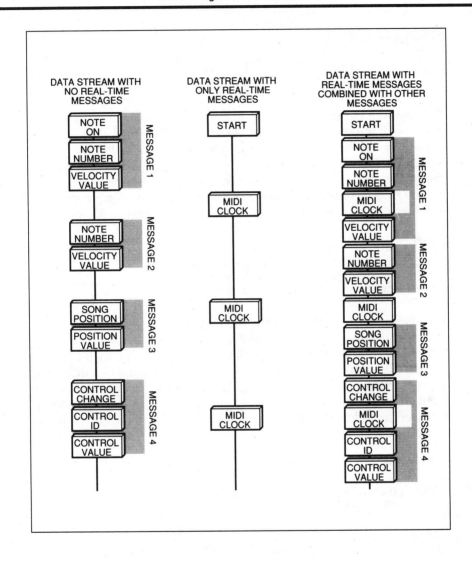

Timing Clock

Byte	Hex	Binary	Description
1	F8	1111 1000	**Status**

This message is used as a timing pulse by MIDI sequencers and drum machines. It is transmitted 24 times per quarter-note. Timing Clocks can be sent even while the transmitter is idle. If this is done, they should be sent at the active tempo setting of the device. This allows receiving instruments to synchronize their internal clocks while waiting for the next Start or Continue message. The receiver's sequence should advance 1/24th of a quarter-note (one note of a 32nd-note triplet) with each Timing Clock received .

Start

Byte	Hex	Binary	Description
1	FA	1111 1010	**Status**

This message is transmitted when the Play or Start button of the master sequencer or drum machine is pushed. Once the message is received, the device resets its internal song position to 0 and begins to play at the reception of the next Timing Clock message. There should be a delay of at least one millisecond between the transmission of the Start message and the Timing Clock message to give the receiver time to respond. The receiver, however, should be able to start immediately, even if the delay is less than one millisecond.

Continue

Byte	Hex	Binary	Description
1	FB	1111 1011	**Status**

This message is transmitted whenever the Continue button of the master sequencer or drum machine is pushed. When the message is received, a previously stopped sequencer or drum machine will begin playing again from the current song position. This will be either the point in the sequence where the last Stop command was received, or a song position value conveyed by a Song Position Pointer message. The receiver does not start the sequence until it receives the next Timing Clock message. There should be a delay of at least one millisecond between the Continue and Timing Clock messages to give the receiver time to respond. The receiver, however, should be able to start immediately, even if the delay between the Continue and Timing Clock is less than one millisecond.

Stop

Byte	Hex	Binary	Description
1	FC	1111 1100	Status

This message is transmitted whenever the Stop button of the master sequencer or drum machine is pushed. The receiver should stop playing its sequence immediately upon receipt of this message. The receiver should also stop incrementing its internal song position if more Timing Clocks are received. The current song position is maintained so the internal sequence can begin from the point at which it was stopped if a Continue message is received. If a Song Position Pointer message is received while the receiver is stopped, the receiver should update its internal song position to the song position value of the message.

When a Stop message is received, any of the receiver's notes which are currently on must be turned off. It is the transmitter's responsibility to track and turn off these "hanging" notes. This is done by sending a corresponding Note Off message for all Note On messages sent before the Stop. An additional All Notes Off message may be sent, but this should never be done instead of sending individual Note Off messages. It is also good practice to reset any controllers to their normal positions. This can be done either by sending individual messages for any controllers that were active when the Stop message was sent, or by sending the Reset All Controllers message.

Active Sensing

Byte	Hex	Binary	Description
1	FE	1111 1110	Status

Transmission and reception of the Active Sensing message is optional. The message is sent every 300 milliseconds (ms) whenever the instrument is idle (not being played) to confirm that the MIDI connection has not been broken. Once a device recognizes Active Sensing, it should anticipate a message of some kind to be received every 300ms. If no messages are received within this time period, the device acts on the assumption that the MIDI cable has been disconnected. At that time, it should turn off any voices that are currently on, and return to normal operation.

System Reset

Byte	Hex	Binary	Description
1	FF	1111 1111	Status

When this message is received, an instrument will return to the *default* settings that are active when it is first turned on. Not all instruments recognize this message. The MIDI specification recommends that this message be used sparingly, and that it be transmitted only by manual control. Do not send the System Reset message automatically on power-up. When it is received, the message should never be echoed (retransmitted through the MIDI Out port). The following list of operations should be performed if the message is recognized.

- Set MIDI Mode to Omni On, Poly (if implemented).
- Set Local Control to on.
- Turn off all voices.
- Reset all controllers.
- Stop sequence playback.
- Set Song Position to 0.
- Clear Running Status buffer.
- Reset all other functions to the power-up condition.

System Exclusive Messages

For programmers and designers, the System Exclusive (SysEx) message is one of the most exciting features of MIDI. This message was originally specified to allow manufacturers the freedom to send and receive any amount of device specific information they felt necessary. The only restriction being that, to avoid confusing other brands of equipment that might be connected via MIDI, each SysEx message must carry a unique manufacturer ID. Because the size of this message was unrestricted, manufacturers began sending complete dumps of their equipment's parameter settings. Programs were then developed to not only save these dumps to mass storage, but to allow retrieval, display, and editing of these settings on any computer. Recently, the SysEx message format has been expanded to include two new Universal formats: Non-Real-Time and Real-Time. To date, Universal SysEx messages for transmitting sample dump data, MIDI Time Code, and device inquiry messages have been defined within these two formats.

General Format of System Exclusive Messages

Byte	Hex	Binary	Description
1	F0	1111 0000	SysEx status
2	ii	0iii iiii	ID number
3	dd	0ddd dddd	first data byte
		.	
		.	any number of data bytes
		.	
n	dd	0ddd dddd	last data byte
n+1	F7	1111 0111	EOX

There are four types of SysEx messages, each of which uses the same general format. The byte following the SysEx status byte is an ID number that indicates the type of SysEx message. Any number of additional data bytes can follow this ID byte. The SysEx message should always be terminated with the 1-byte End Of Exclusive (EOX) message. The following table shows the ID numbers for the different SysEx message types.

SysEx ID Number		SysEx Message Type	Usage
0-124	(00-7CH)	Manufacturer SysEx	device specific
125	(7DH)	Non-Commercial SysEx	research only *
126	(7EH)	Non-Real-Time SysEx	all devices
127	(7FH)	Real-Time SysEx	device

* Note: There is no need to define a format for Non-Commercial SysEx messages.

Manufacturer System Exclusive

Byte	Hex	Binary	Description
1	F0	1111 0000	SysEx status
2	ii	0iii iiii	manufacturer ID number
3	dd	0ddd dddd	first data byte
		.	
		.	any number of data bytes
		.	
n	dd	0ddd dddd	last data byte
n+1	F7	1111 0111	EOX

An ID number between 0-124 (00-7CH) specifies a manufacturer SysEx message. These messages carry device specific data and parameters. An ID number value of 0 signifies a special case. It indicates that the following two bytes will contain the manufacturer ID. This extension makes it possible to have more than the original 124 unique manufacturer ID numbers. The following describes the extended version.

Byte	Hex	Binary	Description
1	F0	1111 0000	SysEx status
2	00	0000 0000	ID extension
3	00	0iii iiii	manufacturer ID byte 1
4	00	0iii iiii	manufacturer ID byte 2
5	dd	0ddd dddd	first data byte
		.	
		.	any number of data bytes
		.	
n	dd	0ddd dddd	last data byte
n+1	F7	1111 0111	EOX

The following table lists all of the currently assigned manufacturer ID numbers.

SysEx Manufacturer ID numbers (1-Byte IDs)

American Group

Number	Manufacturer
01H	Sequential
02H	IDP
03H	Octave-Plateau
04H	Moog
05H	Passport Designs
06H	Lexicon
07H	Kurzweil
08H	Fender
0AH	AKG Acoustics
0BH	Voyce Music
0CH	Waveframe Corp
0DH	ADA Signal Processors
0EH	Garfield Electronics
0FH	Ensoniq
10H	Oberheim
11H	Apple Computer
12H	Grey Matter Response
13H	Mimetics
14H	Palm Tree Instruments
15H	JL Cooper
16H	Lowrey
17H	Adams-Smith
18H	Emu Systems
19H	Harmony Systems
1AH	ART
1BH	Baldwin
1CH	Eventide
1DH	Inventronics
1EH	Key Concepts
1FH	Clarity

European Group

Number	Manufacturer
20H	Passac
21H	Siel
22H	Synthaxe
23H	Stepp
24H	Hohner
25H	Twister
26H	Solton
27H	Jellinghaus MS
28H	Southworth
29H	PPG
2AH	JEN
2BH	SSL Limited
2CH	Audio Veritrieb-P, Struven
2DH	Neve
2EH	Soundtracs Ltd.
2FH	Elka
30H	Dynacord
31H	Intercontinental Electronics
32H	Drawmer
33H	Clavia Digital Instruments
34H	Zyklus Limited
35H	General Electro Music
36H	Cheetah Marketing
37H	C.T.M
38H	Simmons
39H	Soundcraft Electronics
3AH	Steinberg Digital Audio
3BH	Wersi

Japanese Group

Number	Manufacturer
40H	Kawai
41H	Roland
42H	Korg
43H	Yamaha
44H	Casio
45H	Moridaira
46H	Kamiya Studio
47H	Akai
48H	Japan Victor
49H	Mesosha
4AH	Hoshino Gakki
4BH	Fujitsu Electronics
4CH	Sony
4DH	Nisshin Onpa
4EH	TEAC Corp
4FH	System Product
50H	Matsushita Electric
51H	Fostex

SysEx Manufacturer ID numbers (3-Byte IDs)

Number			Manufacturer
00H	00H	07H	Digital Music Corp
00H	00H	08H	IOTA Systems
00H	00H	0BH	IVL Technologies
00H	00H	0CH	Southern Music Systems
00H	00H	0DH	Lake Butler Sound Co.
00H	00H	10H	DOD Electronics
00H	00H	14H	Fretworks
00H	00H	15H	KAT
00H	00H	16H	Opcode
00H	00H	18H	Spatial Sound
00H	00H	19H	KMX
00H	00H	1CH	360 Systems
00H	00H	20H	Axxes
00H	00H	21H	Orban

Universal Non-Real-Time System Exclusive

Byte	Hex	Binary		Description
1	F0	1111	0000	SysEx status
2	7E	0111	1110	non real-time ID
3	cc	0ccc	cccc	device ID number
4	ii	0iii	iiii	sub-id #1
5	ii	0iii	iiii	sub-id #2
6	dd	0ddd	dddd	first data byte
		.		
		.		any number of data bytes
		.		
n	dd	0ddd	dddd	last data byte
n+1	F7	1111	0111	EOX

The currently defined Non-Real-Time messages specify handshaking proto-col, universal sample data dumps, and cueing messages for MIDI Time Code. Universal Non-Real-Time SysEx messages are not device-specific — they can be implemented in any MIDI device at the discretion of the manufacturer. The general format of these messages consists of a header, followed by a block of any number of data bytes, and a terminating EOX. The header will contain either four or five bytes, depending on whether the specific message uses one or two sub-ID bytes. (The first Non-Real-Time messages defined had only one sub-ID byte. All subsequently defined messages use two. The general format of a two sub-ID message is shown above.

Following the SysEx status byte is the Universal Non-Real-Time ID number (7EH). The device ID byte specifies the unit within the system for which the message is intended (0-127). A device ID value of 127 is a special case which indicates that the message is intended for all units in a system. The sub-ID bytes identify the specific Non-Real-Time message as shown in the follow-ing table.

Sub-ID #1	Sub-ID #2	Message
00H	—	unused
01H	not used	Sample Dump Header
02H	not used	Sample Dump Data Packet
03H	not used	Sample Dump Request
04H	nn	MIDI Time Code Set-Up
	00H	Special
	01H	Punch In Points
	02H	Punch OutPoints
	03H	Delete Punch In Point
	04H	Delete Punch Out Point
	05H	Event Start Point
	06H	Event Stop Point
	07H	Event Start Point with additional info
	08H	Event Stop Point with additional info
	09H	Delete Event Start Point
	0AH	Delete Event Stop Point
	0BH	Cue Points
	0CH	Cue Points with additional info
	0DH	Delete Cue Point
	0EH	Event Name in additional info
05H	nn	Sample Dump Extensions
	01H	Multiple Loop Points
	02H	Loop Points Request
06H	nn	Inquiry Message
	01H	Device Inquiry
	02H	Device ID
07-7BH	—	undefined
7CH	not used	Wait
7DH	not used	Cancel
7EH	not used	NAK
7FH	not used	ACK

Device Inquiry

Byte	Hex	Binary	Description
1	F0	1111 0000	SysEx status
2	7E	0111 1110	non-real-time ID
3	cc	0ccc cccc	device ID number
4	06	0000 0110	General Information
4	01	0000 0001	Device Inquiry
5	F7	1111 0111	EOX

This message allows a transmitter to request the identity of receivers in a MIDI system. A receiver should recognize and respond to the message if the value of the device ID byte is 127 (7FH), or if its own internal device ID number matches the device ID value in the inquiry message. Upon recognition of this message, the receiver should respond with the Device Inquiry message.

Device ID

Byte	Hex	Binary	Description
1	F0	1111 0000	SysEx status
2	7E	0111 1110	non real-time ID
3	cc	0ccc cccc	device ID number
4	06	0000 0110	General Information
5	02	0000 0001	Device ID
6	mm	0mmm mmmm	manufacturer ID
7	ff	0fff ffff	device family code LSB
8	ff	0fff ffff	device family code MSB
9	dd	0ddd dddd	family member code LSB
10	dd	0ddd dddd	family member code MSB
11	ss	0sss ssss	software revision level
12	ss	0sss ssss	(format is device
13	ss	0sss ssss	specific)
14	ss	0sss ssss	
15	F7	1111 0111	EOX

This message is sent in response to the Device Inquiry message. Note that, if the manufacturer ID is 0, then two additional bytes are added to handle the extended ID number. (See *Manufacturer System Exclusive*). Following is an example of a Device ID message as it would be transmitted from a Korg M1 set for MIDI channel 1.

Byte	Hex	Binary		Description
1	F0	1111	0000	SysEx status
2	7E	0111	1110	non-real-time ID
3	00	0000	0000	device ID
4	06	0000	0110	General Information
5	02	0000	0001	Device ID
6	42	0100	0010	Korg ID
7	19	0001	1001	M1 family code LSB
8	ff	0000	0000	M1 family code MSB
9	dd	0000	0000	M1 member code LSB
10	dd	0000	0000	M1 member code MSB
11	ss	0sss	ssss	ROM No.
12	00	0000	0000	
13	ss	0sss	ssss	Software Version
14	00	0000	0000	
15	F7	1111	0111	EOX

Sample Dump Request

Byte	Hex	Binary		Description
1	F0	1111	0000	SysEx status
2	7E	0111	1110	non-real-time ID
3	cc	0ccc	cccc	device ID number
4	03	0000	0011	Sample Dump Request
5	ss	0sss	ssss	requested sample number LSB
6	ss	0sss	ssss	requested sample number MSB
7	F7	1111	0111	EOX

This message is sent to request the transmission of sample data from a receiver. When this message is received, the receiving device should check the value of the requested sample number. If it is within the legal range of the receiver's sample numbers, the requested sample is made the current sound and dumped via MIDI to the requesting device. If the sample number is not within the receiver's legal range, the request should be ignored.

Sample Dump Header

Byte	Hex	Binary	Description
1	F0	1111 0000	SysEx status
2	7E	0111 1110	non-real-time ID
3	cc	0ccc cccc	device ID number
4	01	0000 0001	Sample Dump Header
5	ss	0sss ssss	sample number LSB
6	ss	0sss ssss	sample number MSB
7	ee	000e eeee	sample format
8	ff	0fff ffff	sample period LSB
9	ff	0fff ffff	sample period
10	ff	0fff ffff	sample period MSB
11	gg	0ggg gggg	sample length LSB
12	gg	0ggg gggg	sample length
13	gg	0ggg gggg	sample length MSB
14	hh	0hhh hhhh	sus. loop start word LSB
15	hh	0hhh hhhh	sus. loop start word
16	hh	0hhh hhhh	sus. loop start word MSB
17	ii	0iii iiii	sus. loop end word LSB
18	ii	0iii iiii	sus. loop end word
19	ii	0iii iiii	sus. loop end word MSB
20	jj	0jjj jjjj	loop type
21	F7	1111 0111	EOX

This is the first message sent in response to a Sample Dump Request. It contains the following data for the requested sample.

- The sample format is sampling resolution given as the number of significant bits in the sampled sound (8-28).

- The sample period is the length, in nanoseconds, of a single sample. (1/sampling rate).

- The sample length is the number of words in the sampled sound.

- The sustain loop start is the location (in sample words) of the first sample in the sustain loop.

- The sustain loop end is the location (in sample words) of the last sample in the sustain loop.

- The loop type indicates one of three possible sample loops: 0=forward only, 1=forward/backward, and 127=no loop

Sample Dump Data Packet

Byte	Hex	Binary		Description
1	F0	1111	0000	SysEx status
2	7E	0111	1110	non-real-time ID
3	cc	0ccc	cccc	device ID number
4	02	0000	0010	Sample Dump Data Packet
5	kk	0kkk	kkkk	running packet count
6	dd	0ddd	dddd	sample data byte 1
		.		
		.		sample data bytes 2-119
		.		
125	dd	0ddd	dddd	sample data byte 120
126	ll	0ddd	dddd	checksum
127	F7	1111	0111	EOX

Sample data is sent in a series of Sample Dump Data Packet messages. Each message consists of a 4-byte header, packet count, 120 bytes of data, checksum, and EOX. The packet count begins at 0 and increments with each additional packet sent. The packet count resets to 0 after reaching 127. The receiver uses the packet count to distinguish a new packet from a resend of the previous packet.

The number of sample words held in the 120-byte data block depends on the sample format. There are 60 words in the block if the sample format is 8-14 bits (two bytes per word), 40 words in the block if the sample format is 15-21 bits (three bytes per word), and 30 words in the block if the sample format is 22-28 bits (four bytes per word). Words are sent MSB first. Sample data is left-justified in the 7-bit bytes. Unused bits are filled with zeros. For example, FFFH would be sent as 01111111 01111000 (binary). (See *Part 4: SysEx Data*.) FFFH represents full positive 12-bit value and 00H represents full negative value. The checksum is the exclusive-or (XOR) of bytes 2-125 of the message.

Sample Dump Loop Points Request

Byte	Hex	Binary	Description
1	F0	1111 0000	SysEx status
2	7E	0111 1110	non-real-time ID
3	cc	0ccc cccc	device ID number
4	05	0000 0101	Additional Loop Information
5	02	0000 0010	Loop Points Request
6	ss	0sss ssss	sample number LSB
7	ss	0sss ssss	sample number MSB
8	bb	0bbb bbbb	loop number LSB
9	bb	0bbb bbbb	loop number MSB
10	F7	1111 0111	EOX

This message is used to request information about a specific loop in a sample. One advantage of using the loop request and response messages is that loop data can be acquired without having to retransmit the entire sample. Another advantage is that the loop messages can provide information about any (or all) loops in a sample. The Sample Dump Header contains data for only one — the sustain loop. Upon receiving this message, the receiver should respond by sending a Multiple Loop Points message for the requested loop number of the sample. Loop number 00 00H is the sustain loop specified in the Sample Dump Data Header. Loop number 7F 7FH is a special case meaning "request all loops." When the message is received, the receiver should respond by sending a Multiple Loop Points message for each loop in the requested sample

Sample Dump Multiple Loop Points

Byte	Hex	Binary	Description
1	F0	1111 0000	SysEx status
2	7E	0111 1110	non-real-time ID
3	cc	0ccc cccc	device ID number
4	05	0000 0101	Additional Loop Information
5	01	0000 0001	Multiple Loop messages
6	ss	0sss ssss	sample number LSB
7	ss	0sss ssss	sample number MSB
8	bb	0bbb bbbb	loop number LSB
9	bb	0bbb bbbb	loop number MSB
10	cc	0ccc cccc	loop type
11	dd	0ddd dddd	loop start address LSB
12	dd	0ddd dddd	loop start address
13	dd	0ddd dddd	loop start address MSB
14	ee	0eee eeee	loop end address LSB
15	ee	0eee eeee	loop end address
16	ee	0eee eeee	loop end address MSB
17	F7	1111 0111	EOX

This message is sent in response to the Loop Points Request message. One Multiple Loop Points message is sent for each requested loop (except for "delete all loops", which only requires a single message).

- The loop number is the number of a specific loop in the sample. Loop 00 00H is the sustain loop. Loop 7F 7F is a special case meaning "delete all loops."

- The loop start is the location (in sample words) of the first sample in the loop.

- The loop end is the location (in sample words) of the last sample in the loop.

- The loop type indicates one of three possible sample loops: 0=forward only, 1=forward/backward, and 127=no loop.

ACK

Byte	Hex	Binary		Description
1	F0	1111	0000	SysEx status
2	7E	0111	1110	non-real-time ID
3	cc	0ccc	cccc	device ID number
4	7F	0111	1111	ACK
5	pp	0ppp	pppp	packet number
6	F7	1111	0111	EOX

This handshaking message is used as a flag to acknowledge that the last data packet was received with no errors.

NAK

Byte	Hex	Binary		Description
1	F0	1111	0000	SysEx status
2	7E	0111	1110	non-real-time ID
3	cc	0ccc	cccc	device ID number
4	7E	0111	1110	NAK
5	pp	0ppp	pppp	packet number
6	F7	1111	0111	EOX

This handshaking message is used as a flag to indicate that an error was detected on reception of the last data packet.

Wait

Byte	Hex	Binary		Description
1	F0	1111	0000	SysEx status
2	7E	0111	1110	non-real-time ID
3	cc	0ccc	cccc	device ID number
4	7C	0111	1100	Wait
5	pp	0ppp	pppp	packet number
6	F7	1111	0111	EOX

This handshaking message is used to halt a sample dump in progress. Upon receipt of a Wait message, the receiver should stop sending data packets and wait indefinitely for the next message from the sender of the Wait. The dump should continue if an ACK is received and should abort if Cancel (or any message other than ACK) is received. Note that the receiver of this message should wait indefinitely for the next message — not time out. The Wait message is typically sent to allow the transmitter to access a disk or to perform internal calculations or other time-consuming tasks. There is no way to know how long the receiver may have to wait before continuing with the dump.

Cancel

Byte	Hex	Binary		Description
1	F0	1111	0000	SysEx status
2	7E	0111	1110	non-real-time ID
3	cc	0ccc	cccc	device ID number
4	7D	0111	1101	Cancel
5	pp	0ppp	pppp	packet number
6	F7	1111	0111	EOX

This handshaking message is used as a flag to abort a dump in progess. Upon receipt of the message the receiver should respond by aborting the dump and returning to normal operation.

MIDI Time Code Set-Up Messages

Byte	Hex	Binary	Description
1	F0	1111 0000	SysEx status
2	7E	0111 1110	non-real-time ID
3	cc	0ccc cccc	device ID number
4	04	0000 0011	MTC Set-Up
5	tt	0ttt tttt	Setup Type
6	bc	0bbc cccc	SMPTE format / hours
7	dd	00dd dddd	minutes
8	ee	00ee eeee	seconds
9	ff	000f ffff	frames
10	gg	0ggg gggg	fractional frames
11	ii	0iii iiii	event number LSB
12	ii	0iii iiii	event number MSB
			additional info (optional)
13	0l	0000 1111	first low nibble
14	0h	0000 hhh	first high nibble
		.	
		. any number	of nibblized bytes
		.	
n	0l	0000 1111	last low nibble
n+1	0h	0000 hhh	last high nibble
n+2	F7	1111 0111	EOX

MIDI Time Code Set-Up messages are used to transmit event information to devices that implement MTC. There are two types of events, continuous and one-shot. A continuous event is one that continues to run until stopped with an Event Stop message (a sequence, for example). A one-shot event is one that stops by itself (a sound-effect, for example). In MTC messages, a one-shot event is referred to as a *cue*, and a running event is simply referred to as an *event*. All of the cues and events to be played by a device are held in an event list. The event list is simply a record of event and cue numbers and the SMPTE locations of when they start and stop. Each event or cue number refers to a specific sound (or effect, fader move, etc.) stored in the device. (This is similar to a MIDI program number or song select number.) The same event or cue may be used more than once in a given event list and will be referred to by the same event number. Note, though, that the start and stop times will be different for each occurrence.

The general formats for these messages are given in the preceding table. The time bytes in the messages are used to specify event times. The event time is the SMPTE location where the message-specific event occurs. The event number bytes specify one of 16,834 unique events for each Set-Up type. The formats and descriptions of the 19 Set-Up messages currently defined follow.

Special

Byte	Hex	Binary		Description
1	F0	1111	0000	SysEx status
2	7E	0111	1110	non-real-time ID
3	cc	0ccc	cccc	device ID number
4	04	0000	0011	MTC Set-Up
5	00	0000	0000	Special
6	bc	0bbc	cccc	SMPTE format / hours
7	dd	00dd	dddd	minutes
8	ee	00ee	eeee	seconds
9	ff	000f	ffff	frames
10	gg	0ggg	gggg	fractional frames
11	ii	0iii	iiii	Special Type ID LSB
12	ii	0iii	iiii	Special Type ID MSB
13	F7	1111	0111	EOX

Special messages carry data pertaining to the global settings of a device. Six Special Set-Up messages are currently defined. Each is identified by a 2-byte Special Type ID placed in the event number bytes. The six Special messages are:

00 00   Time Code Offset
This is used to send a relative Time Code offset value to devices in the system.

01 00   Enable Event List
This message signals a device to enable execution of the events in its list when their corresponding MTC or SMPTE times occur. The time bytes in the message are ignored.

02 00   Disable Event List
This message signals a device to disable (mute) its event list without erasing it. The time bytes in the message are ignored.

03 00   Clear Event List

This message signals a device to erase its entire event list. The time bytes in the message are ignored.

04 00   System Stop

This message is used to send a Time Code reference to specify when a device may shut down. It is a safety feature to prohibit Event Starts without matching Event Stops, and to prevent tape machines from running past the end of a reel.

05 00   Event List Request

This message is sent from the MTC master. If the receiver's device ID matches the device ID value in the message, the receiver responds by transmitting its event list as a series of Set-Up messages, beginning at the SMPTE time held in the time bytes of the Event List Request message.

Punch In/Out

Byte	Hex	Binary	Description
1	F0	1111 0000	SysEx status
2	7E	0111 1110	non-real-time ID
3	cc	0ccc cccc	device ID number
4	04	0000 0011	MTC Set-Up
5	01	0000 0001	Punch In = 01
			Punch Out = 02
6	bc	0bbc cccc	SMPTE format / hours
7	dd	00dd dddd	minutes
8	ee	00ee eeee	seconds
9	ff	000f ffff	frames
10	gg	0ggg gggg	fractional frames
11	ii	0iii iiii	track number LSB
12	ii	0iii iiii	track number MSB
13	F7	1111 0111	EOX

This message is used to set up a punch in (start recording) or punch out (stop recording) on a specific track of the receiving device at a specified SMPTE time. The value of the Set-Up Type byte (byte 5) indicates whether to punch in (01H) or punch out (02H). The time bytes hold the SMPTE time where the punch in/out occurs. The event number indicates the track number where the punch in/out is to occur.

Delete Punch In/Out

Byte	Hex	Binary	Description
1	F0	1111 0000	SysEx status
2	7E	0111 1110	non-real-time ID
3	cc	0ccc cccc	device ID number
4	04	0000 0011	MTC Set-Up
5	03	0000 0011	Delete Punch In = 03
			Delete Punch Out = 04
6	bc	0bbc cccc	SMPTE format / hours
7	dd	00dd dddd	minutes
8	ee	00ee eeee	seconds
9	ff	000f ffff	frames
10	gg	0ggg gggg	fractional frames
11	ii	0iii iiii	track number LSB
12	ii	0iii iiii	track number MSB
13	F7	1111 0111	EOX

This message is used to delete a matching punch in/out point from the receiver's event list. The value of the Set-Up Type byte (byte 5) indicates whether to delete a punch in (03H) or a punch out (04H). The time bytes hold the SMPTE time where the punch in/out to be deleted occurs. The event number indicates the track number.

Event Start/Stop

Byte	Hex	Binary	Description
1	F0	1111 0000	SysEx status
2	7E	0111 1110	non-real-time ID
3	cc	0ccc cccc	device ID number
4	04	0000 0011	MTC Set-Up
5	05	0000 0100	Event Start =05
			Event Stop = 06
6	bc	0bbc cccc	SMPTE format / hours
7	dd	00dd dddd	minutes
8	ee	00ee eeee	seconds
9	ff	000f ffff	frames
10	gg	0ggg gggg	fractional frames
11	ii	0iii iiii	event number LSB
12	ii	0iii iiii	event number MSB
13	F7	1111 0111	EOX

This message is used to tell the receiving device to cue-up a specific event to start or stop at a specific SMPTE time when Time Code begins running. The value of the Set-Up Type byte (byte 5) indicates whether the event is to be started (05H) or stopped (06H). The time bytes hold the SMPTE time at which the start or stop occurs. The event number indicates the specific event (local to the receiver) to be started or stopped. Note that this is used for events such as sequences or for very long samples which, once started, will continue until explicitly stopped. For short duration events such as a single gun-shot sound effect, the Cue Point message is used.

Event Start/Stop with Additional Information

Byte	Hex	Binary	Description
1	F0	1111 0000	SysEx status
2	7E	0111 1110	non-real-time ID
3	cc	0ccc cccc	device ID number
4	04	0000 0011	MTC Set-Up
5	07	0000 0111	Event Start + Info = 07
			Event Stop + Info = 08
6	bc	0bbc cccc	SMPTE format / hours
7	dd	00dd dddd	minutes
8	ee	00ee eeee	seconds
9	ff	000f ffff	frames
10	gg	0ggg gggg	fractional frames
11	ii	0iii iiii	event number LSB
12	ii	0iii iiii	event number MSB
13	01	0000 1111	first low nibble
14	0h	0000 hhhh	first high nibble
		.	
		. any number	of nibblized MIDI bytes
		.	
n	01	0000 1111	last low nibble
n+1	0h	0000 hhhh	last high nibble
n+2	F7	1111 0111	EOX

This message is a variation of the Event Start/Stop message previously described. It is also used to cue-up a specific event. Any number of additional information bytes can be inserted between the event number MSB and EOX bytes. The additional information is formatted as a nibblized MIDI data stream, LS nibble first. The additional data can be used for such things as setting a volume level or altering the effects parameters of the receiver.

Delete Event Start/Stop

Byte	Hex	Binary	Description
1	F0	1111 0000	SysEx status
2	7E	0111 1110	non-real-time ID
3	cc	0ccc cccc	device ID number
4	04	0000 0011	MTC Set-Up
5	09	0000 1001	Delete Event Start = 09
			Delete Event Stop = 0A
6	bc	0bbc cccc	SMPTE format / hours
7	dd	00dd dddd	minutes
8	ee	00ee eeee	seconds
9	ff	000f ffff	frames
10	gg	0ggg gggg	fractional frames
11	ii	0iii iiii	event number LSB
12	ii	0iii iiii	event number MSB
13	F7	1111 0111	EOX

This message is used to delete a matching event from the receiver's event list. The value of the Set-Up Type byte (byte 5) indicates whether to delete an event start (09H) or an event stop(0AH).

Cue Point

Byte	Hex	Binary	Description
1	F0	1111 0000	SysEx status
2	7E	0111 1110	non-real-time ID
3	cc	0ccc cccc	device ID number
4	04	0000 0011	MTC Set-Up
5	0B	0000 1011	Cue Point
6	bc	0bbc cccc	SMPTE format / hours
7	dd	00dd dddd	minutes
8	ee	00ee eeee	seconds
9	ff	000f ffff	frames
10	gg	0ggg gggg	fractional frames
11	ii	0iii iiii	event number LSB
12	ii	0iii iiii	event number MSB
13	F7	1111 0111	EOX

This message is used to tell the receiving device to cue up a one-shot event to occur at a specific SMPTE time when Time Code begins running. The time bytes hold the SMPTE time at which the event occurs. The event number indicates the specific event (local to the receiver). Use this message for short duration events that will stop by themselves, such as sound effects.

Cue Point with Additional Info

Byte	Hex	Binary	Description
1	F0	1111 0000	SysEx status
2	7E	0111 1110	non-real-time ID
3	cc	0ccc cccc	device ID number
4	04	0000 0011	MTC Set-Up
5	0C	0000 1100	Cue Point + Info
6	bc	0bbc cccc	SMPTE format / hours
7	dd	00dd dddd	minutes
8	ee	00ee eeee	seconds
9	ff	000f ffff	frames
10	gg	0ggg gggg	fractional frames
11	ii	0iii iiii	event number LSB
12	ii	0iii iiii	event number MSB
13	01	0000 1111	first low nibble
14	0h	0000 hhhh	first high nibble
		.	
		. any number	of nibblized MIDI bytes
		.	
n	01	0000 1111	last low nibble
n+1	0h	0000 hhhh	last high nibble
n+2	F7	1111 0111	EOX

This message is a variation of the Cue Point message and is also used to cue-up a specific one-shot event. Any number of additional information bytes can be inserted between the event number MSB and EOX bytes. The additional information is formatted as a nibblized MIDI data stream, LS nibble first. The additional data can be used for such things as setting a volume level or altering the effects parameters of the receiver.

Delete Cue Point

Byte	Hex	Binary	Description
1	F0	1111 0000	SysEx status
2	7E	0111 1110	non-real-time ID
3	cc	0ccc cccc	device ID number
4	04	0000 0011	MTC Set-Up
5	0D	0000 1101	Delete Cue Point
6	bc	0bbc cccc	SMPTE format / hours
7	dd	00dd dddd	minutes
8	ee	00ee eeee	seconds
9	ff	000f ffff	frames
10	gg	0ggg gggg	fractional frames
11	ii	0iii iiii	event number LSB
12	ii	0iii iiii	event number MSB
13	F7	1111 0111	EOX

This message is used to delete a matching cue from the receiver's event list.

Event Name in Additional Info

Byte	Hex	Binary	Description
1	F0	1111 0000	SysEx status
2	7E	0111 1110	non real-time ID
3	cc	0ccc cccc	device ID number
4	04	0000 0011	MTC Set-Up
5	0E	0000 1110	Event Name In Info
6	bc	0bbc cccc	SMPTE format / hours
7	dd	00dd dddd	minutes
8	ee	00ee eeee	seconds
9	ff	000f ffff	frames
10	gg	0ggg gggg	fractional frames
11	ii	0iii iiii	event number LSB
12	ii	0iii iiii	event number MSB
13	01	0000 1111	first low nibble
14	0h	0000 hhhh	first high nibble
		.	
		. any number	of nibblized ASCII bytes
		.	
n	01	0000 1111	last low nibble
n+1	0h	0000 hhhh	last high nibble
n+2	F7	1111 0111	EOX

This message is used to assign text information to a given event number. The additional information is formatted as nibblized ASCII, LS nibble first. The operator can use this addtional data as an aid for logging cue information into the receiver. The conventions for implementing newline, carriage return and line feed follow.

Action	ASCII Character
Line Feed	LF
Carriage Return	CR
New Line	CR + LF

Universal Real-Time SysEx

Byte	Hex	Binary		Description
1	F0	1111	0000	SysEx status
2	7F	0111	1111	real-time ID
3	cc	0ccc	cccc	device ID number
4	ii	0iii	iiii	sub-id #1
5	ii	0iii	iiii	sub-id #2
6	dd	0ddd	dddd	first data byte
		.		
		.		any number of data bytes
		.		
n	dd	0ddd	dddd	last data byte
n+1	F7	1111	0111	EOX

Universal Real-Time System Exclusive messages are not device-specific. They can be implemented in any device at the option of the manufacturer. The general format of these messages consists of a 5-byte header followed by any number of data bytes and a terminating EOX. Two Universal Real-Time messages are currently defined. Both of these, Full Message and User Bits, are part of the MIDI Time Code standard.

MIDI Time Code Full Message

Byte	Hex	Binary		Description
1	F0	1111	0000	SysEx status
2	7F	0111	1111	real-time ID
3	cc	0ccc	cccc	device ID number
4	01	0000	0001	MIDI Time Code
5	01	0000	0001	MTC Full Message
6	bc	0bbc	cccc	SMPTE format / hours
7	dd	00dd	dddd	minutes
8	ee	00ee	eeee	seconds
9	ff	000f	ffff	frames
10	F7	1111	0111	EOX

This message is transmitted to update SMPTE Time when the master tape machine is in fast forward, rewind, or shuttle mode. In these high-speed "search" modes, it isn't necessary to maintain synchronization between the master tape and connected slaves. The Full Message is used to allow the receiving device(s) to locate the point at which to begin playing once the master tape is returned to play mode. The SMPTE time in the time bytes of this message takes effect upon the arrival of the next Quarter-Frame message.

MIDI Time Code User Bits

Byte	Hex	Binary	Description
1	F0	1111 0000	SysEx status
2	7F	0111 1111	real-time ID
3	cc	0ccc cccc	device ID number
4	01	0000 0001	MIDI Time Code
5	02	0000 0010	User Bits
6	0a	0000 aaaa	SMPTE Binary Group 1
6	0b	0000 bbbb	SMPTE Binary Group 2
6	0c	0000 cccc	SMPTE Binary Group 3
6	0d	0000 dddd	SMPTE Binary Group 4
6	0e	0000 eeee	SMPTE Binary Group 5
6	0f	0000 ffff	SMPTE Binary Group 6
6	0g	0000 gggg	SMPTE Binary Group 7
6	0h	0000 hhhh	SMPTE Binary Group 8
6	0i	0000 00ii	Binary Group Flag Bits
10	F7	1111 0111	EOX

This message is used whenever SMPTE "User Bits" must be transferred to MTC devices. User Bits are 32 bits specified by SMPTE. Their functions are application-specific, and can be programmed only by equipment designed for particular functions. They can be used, for example, to tag a tape with a date code or reel number. The following table shows how the nine data bytes of the message are denibblized into the four 8-bit characters and the 2-bit format code specified by SMPTE.

Char.	Hex	Binary	Description
1	ab	aaaa bbbb	SMPTE Binary Group 1 + 2
2	cd	cccc dddd	SMPTE Binary Group 3 + 4
3	ef	eeee ffff	SMPTE Binary Group 5 + 6
4	gh	gggg hhhh	SMPTE Binary Group 7 + 8
5	0i	0000 00ii	SMPTE Format Code

Implementation Notes

Running Status

The MIDI Specification defines a special time-saving format for transmitting Channel Voice and Channel Mode messages called Running Status. Transmission of data in Running Status format is optional. However, all devices must be able to process data received in Running Status format. In the normal MIDI format, each message is transmitted in its entirety. For each message, its status byte is sent first, followed by all of the data bytes defined for the message. For example, a Note On message is sent as three bytes: one status byte and two data bytes. Therefore, sending two Note Ons would require the transmission of six bytes. Sending three Note Ons would require nine bytes, and so on.

When the optional Running Status format is used, it isn't necessary to send redundant status bytes. Sending a single Note On message would still require three bytes, but each addtional Note On message sent would only require two bytes, as shown in the following illustration. It is possible to transmit Note On and Note Off messages in the same Running Status stream, since the Note On zero velocity message is synonymous with the Note Off message.

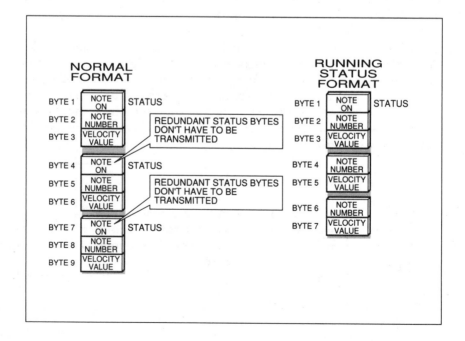

Running Status transmission is particularly useful when long strings of messages with the same status must be sent. For example, moving a 7-bit continuous controller through its full range would result in the transmission of 128 Control Change messages over a very short period of time. The normal format would require sending 384 bytes: 128 increments x 3 bytes, while Running Status format requires only 257 bytes: 1 status byte + (128 increments x 2 bytes).

It is the receiver's responsibility to identify and process Running Status transmissions. To do this, the receiver should always hold the last received status byte in a Running Status *buffer*.

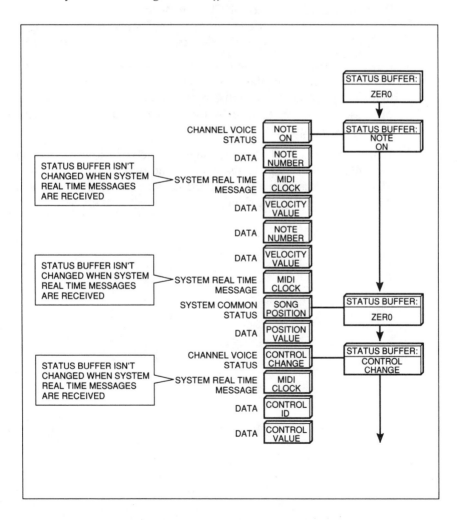

The receiver must also keep track of how many data bytes are required for each message. (See *Parsing MIDI Data*.) MIDI data bytes are then processed according to the value of the Running Status buffer. The following guidelines are recommended when implementing a Running Status buffer.

- Clear the buffer on power-up.

- Process incoming data bytes as indicated by the value of the buffer. While the buffer value is zero, ignore incoming data bytes. When the buffer value is not equal to zero, its content will be the value of the last received Channel Voice or Channel Mode status byte.

- When *any* Channel Voice or Channel Mode message is received, store its status in the buffer. (This includes Channel Mode messages designated for a channel other than the receiver's basic channel.)

- If a System Exclusive or System Common status is received, clear the buffer. (This includes the two undefined System Common status bytes.) The System Exclusive or System Common message is processed if it is recognized by the device, otherwise subsequent data bytes are ignored.

- When a System Real-Time message is received, do not alter the contents of the buffer. (This includes the two undefined System Real-Time status bytes.) The System Real Time message is processed if it is recognized by the device.

MIDI Modes

It is possible for a single device to transmit and receive in different modes. A single device may also transmit and receive on different channels. It is also possible for a single device to function as more than one "virtual" instrument, with each instrument functioning as an independent, polyphonic sound source. In this case, each of the device's instruments can be assigned its own basic channel and mode. This type of operation is commonly referred to as "Multi-Mode," but it is not technically a MIDI mode. A brief summary of the four MIDI modes is given below.

Mode 1 (Omni On/Poly)

In this mode, a transmitter is polyphonic. It may send Channel Voice messages for more than one voice at a time. All of these messages are sent on its assigned basic channel. A receiver recognizes Channel Voice messages from any channel and assigns them polyphonically to its internal voices.

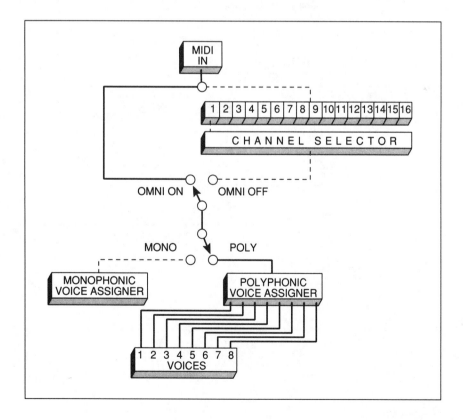

Mode 2 (Omni On/Mono)

In this mode, a transmitter is monophonic. It sends Channel Voice messages for only one voice at a time. These messages are sent on its assigned basic channel. A receiver recognizes Channel Voice messages from any channel and assigns them to one monophonic voice.

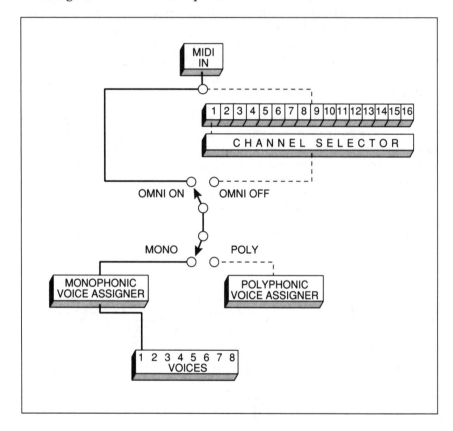

Mode 3 (Omni Off/Poly)

In this mode, a transmitter is polyphonic. It may send Channel Voice messages for more than one voice at a time. All of these messages are sent on its basic Channel. A receiver recognizes only those Channel messages on the same channel as its basic channel and assigns them polyphonically to its internal voices.

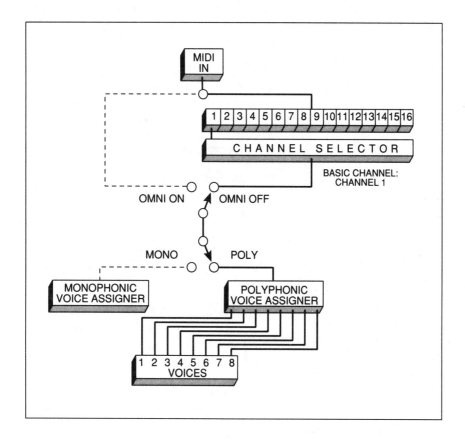

Mode 4 (Omni Off/Mono)

In this mode, the transmitter acts as one or more monophonic transmitters. It may send Channel Voice messages for more than one voice at a time, but each monophonic voice is sent on a separate channel. Mode 4 is commonly implemented in guitar and percussion controllers—allowing each string or percussion pedal to transmit on separate channels. A receiver recognizes Voice Channel messages on a range of channels. The range is one channel for each of its internal voices, beginning with its assigned basic channel. (See *Mono On* for details on implementation.)

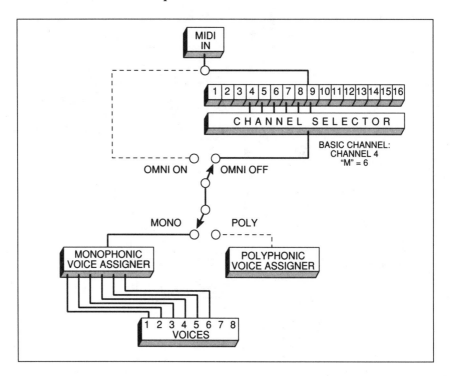

Response to Mode Messages

Regardless of its current mode, a receiver should respond to Mode messages that are on its assigned basic channel. It should ignore Mode messages on channels other than the basic channel. If a message is received for a mode not implemented in the receiver, it may either ignore the request, or switch to an alternate mode. If the mode message is ignored, the receiver should also ignore all subsequent Channel Voice messages until it receives a Mode message it recognizes. The recommended alternate mode for most situations is Mode 1 (Omni On/Poly).

MIDI Clock Timing Diagram

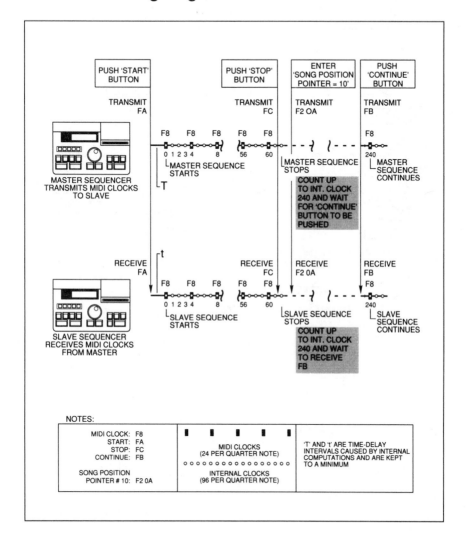

MIDI Time Code Timing Diagram

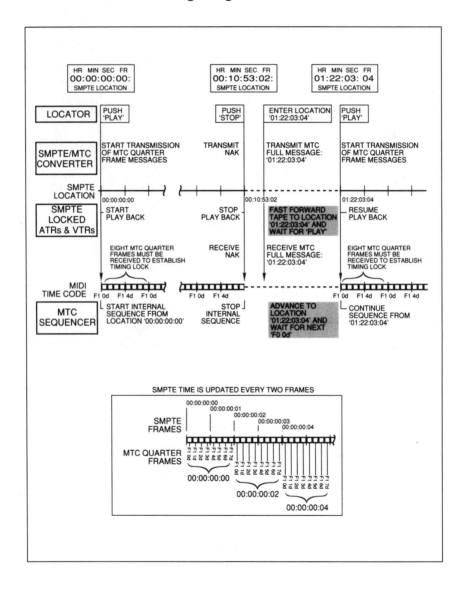

Sample Dump Standard Communication Protocol

The MIDI Sample Dump Standard specifies the exchange of sample dump data in both open loop and closed loop systems. In an open loop system, the MIDI Out port of the device sending sample data is connected to the MIDI In port of the device receiving the data. In a closed loop system, an additional connection is made from the MIDI Out port of the receiving device back to the MIDI In port of the sending device. This allows handshaking between the units to increase speed, allow for error detection and recovery, and to provide a wait mechanism for devices that need extra time to process sample data (disk access, etc.). The previously described ACK, NAK, Wait, and Cancel messages are used as handshaking flags in closed loop transmissions. Following is an outline of the protocol used.

Time Outs

- Minimum TIME OUT after transmission of HEADER is 2 seconds.

- Minimum TIME OUT after transmission of DATA PACKET is 20ms.

Open Loop

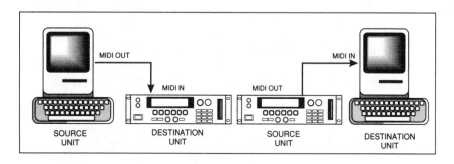

Source Unit	Destination Unit
HEADER ————————————>	
TIME OUT	(no message sent)
(2 second min.)	
DATA PACKET ————————————>	
TIME OUT	(no message sent)
(20 ms. min)	
DATA PACKET ————————————>	

If no message is received during the TIME OUT after the HEADER is sent, or between DATA PACKETs, an open loop is assumed and the next DATA PACKET is sent.

Closed Loop

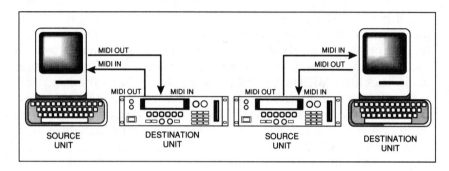

Source Unit	Destination Unit
TIME OUT <————————	message

If a message is received during the TIME OUT (closed loop), the Source Unit acts on the message when it is received as shown below.

Source Unit		Destination Unit
Send next packet <————————		**ACK**
	OR	
Resend packet <————————		**NAK**
	OR	
Halt until next <————————		**WAIT** message
	OR	
Abort dump <————————		**CANCEL**
	OR	
Abort dump <————————		Other message

Sending Samples

Open Loop

```
        Source Unit                    Destination Unit
        HEADER          ————————————————>
        TIME OUT
        (2 second min.)
        DATA PACKET——————————————————>
        TIME OUT
        (20 ms.min)
        DATA PACKET——————————————————>
        TIME OUT
        (20 ms.min)
        DATA PACKET——————————————————>
                        CONTINUE UNTIL
                        ALL PACKETS
                        ARE SENT
```

In an open loop, the Source Unit sends all of the DATA PACKETs with no handshaking.

Closed Loop Example A:

```
        Source sample length < or = Destination sample length

        Source Unit                     Destination Unit
                        <——————————————  DUMP REQUEST
        HEADER          ——————————————>
        TIME OUT        <——————————————   ACK
        DATA PACKET     ——————————————>
        TIME OUT        <——————————————   ACK
        DATA PACKET     ——————————————>
        TIME OUT        <——————————————   ACK
                        <- CONTINUE->
   last DATA PACKET     ——————————————>
        TIME OUT        <——————————————   ACK
        STOP
```

In this closed loop example, handshaking is performed after each packet is accepted. Handshaking should follow transmission of the last packet to acknowledge that no error occurred when the packet was received.

Closed Loop Example B:

Source sample length > Destination sample length

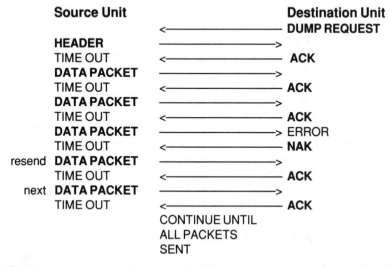

```
          Source Unit                          Destination Unit
                         <-------------------  DUMP REQUEST
          HEADER         ------------------->
          TIME OUT       <-------------------  ACK
          DATA PACKET    ------------------->
          TIME OUT       <-------------------  ACK
          DATA PACKET    ------------------->
          TIME OUT       <-------------------  ACK
                              <- CONTINUE->
          DATA PACKET    ------------------->
          TIME OUT       <-------------------  CANCEL (memory full)
          ABORT
```

In this example, the Destination Unit transmits CANCEL when its memory is full, telling the Source Unit not to send any more DATA PACKETs.

Closed Loop Example C: NAK

```
          Source Unit                          Destination Unit
                         <-------------------  DUMP REQUEST
          HEADER         ------------------->
          TIME OUT       <-------------------  ACK
          DATA PACKET    ------------------->
          TIME OUT       <-------------------  ACK
          DATA PACKET    ------------------->
          TIME OUT       <-------------------  ACK
          DATA PACKET    -------------------> ERROR
          TIME OUT       <-------------------  NAK
 resend   DATA PACKET    ------------------->
          TIME OUT       <-------------------  ACK
 next     DATA PACKET    ------------------->
          TIME OUT       <-------------------  ACK
                         CONTINUE UNTIL
                         ALL PACKETS
                         SENT
```

When a reception error occurs, the Destination Unit transmits NAK, requesting that the last packet be resent. The Source Unit retransmits the packet requested by the NAK if it is capable of doing so. After receiving an ACK for the resent packet, it continues with the dump.

Closed Loop Example D: WAIT

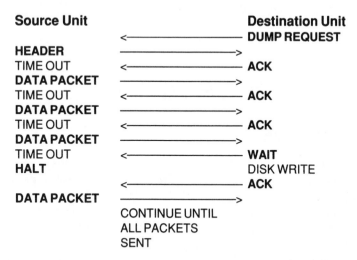

```
     Source Unit                           Destination Unit
                        <———————————————  DUMP REQUEST
     HEADER             ———————————————>
     TIME OUT           <———————————————  ACK
     DATA PACKET        ———————————————>
     TIME OUT           <———————————————  ACK
     DATA PACKET        ———————————————>
     TIME OUT           <———————————————  ACK
     DATA PACKET        ———————————————>
     TIME OUT           <———————————————  WAIT
     HALT                                  DISK WRITE
                        <———————————————  ACK
     DATA PACKET        ———————————————>
                        CONTINUE UNTIL
                        ALL PACKETS
                        SENT
```

If the Source Unit receives a WAIT during a TIME OUT, it halts until another message is received. This frees the Destination Unit to perform any other tasks, such as disk writing, etc. When the Destination Unit is ready to continue the dump, it sends an ACK, as shown in the previous example. It could, alternatively, stop the dump, or request that a packet be resent by transmitting the appropriate CANCEL or NAK.

In this section we have reproduced the Standard MIDI Files 1.0 as published by the International MIDI Association.

Standard MIDI Files 1.0

0 Introduction

The document outlines the specification for MIDI Files. The purpose of MIDI Files is to provide a way of interchanging time-stamped MIDI data between different programs on the same or different computers. One of the primary design goals is compact representation, which makes it very appropriate for a disk-based file format, but which might make it inappropriate for storing in memory for quick access by a sequencer program. (It can be easily converted to a quickly-accessible format on the fly as files are read in or written out.) It is not intended to replace the normal file format of any program, though it could be used for this purpose if desired.

MIDI Files contain one or more MIDI streams, with time information for each event. Song, sequence, and track structures, tempo and time signature information, are all supported. Track names and other descriptive information may be stored with the MIDI data. This format supports multiple tracks and multiple sequences so that if the user of a program which supports multiple tracks intends to move a file to another one, this format can allow that to happen.

This spec defines the 8-bit binary data stream used in the file. The data can be stored in a binary file, nibbleized, 7-bit-ized for efficient MIDI transmission, converted to Hex ASCII, or translated symbolically to a printable text file. This spec addresses what's in the 8-bit stream. It does not address how a MIDI File will be transmitted over MIDI. It is the general feeling that a MIDI transmission protocol will be developed for files in general and MIDI Files will used this scheme.

1 Sequences, Tracks, Chunks: File Block Structure

Conventions

In this document, bit 0 means the least significant bit of a byte, and bit 7 is the most significant.

Some numbers in MIDI Files are represented in a form called a variable-length quantity. These numbers are represented 7 bits per byte, most significant bits first. All bytes except the last have bit 7 set, and the last byte has bit 7 clear. If the number is between 0 and 127, it is thus represented exactly as one byte.

Here are some examples of numbers represented as variable-length quantities:

Number (hex)	Representation (hex)
00000000	00
00000040	40
0000007F	7F
00000080	81 00
00002000	C0 00
00003FFF	FF 7F
00004000	81 80 00
00100000	C0 80 00
001FFFFF	FF FF 7F
00200000	81 80 80 00
08000000	C0 80 80 00
0FFFFFFF	FF FF FF 7F

The largest number which is allowed is 0FFFFFFF so that the variable-length representation must fit in 32 bits in a routine to write variable-length numbers. Theoretically, larger numbers are possible, but 2 x 108 96ths of a beat at a fast tempo of 500 beats per minute is four days, long enough for any delta-time!

Files

To any file system, a MIDI File is simply a series of 8-bit bytes. On the Macintosh, this byte stream is stored in the data fork of a file (with file type 'Midi'), or on the Clipboard (with data type 'Midi'). Most other computers store 8-bit byte streams in files — naming or storage conventions for those computers will be defined as required.

Chunks

MIDI Files are made up of chunks. Each chunk has a 4-character type and a 32-bit length, which is the number of bytes in the chunk. This structure allows future chunk types to be designed which may easily be ignored if encountered by a program written before the chunk type is introduced. Your programs should expect alien chunks and treat them as if they weren't there.

Each chunk begins with a 4-character ASCII type. It is followed by a 32-bit length, most significant byte first (a length of 6 is stored as 00 00 00 06). This length refers to the number of bytes of data which follow: the eight bytes of type and length are not included. Therefore, a chunk with a length of 6 would actually occupy 14 bytes in the disk file.

This chunk architecture is similar to that used by Electronic Arts' IFF format, and the chunks described herein could easily be placed in an IFF file. The MIDI File itself is not an IFF file: it contains no nested chunks, and chunks are not constrained to be an even number of bytes long. Converting it to an IFF file is as easy as padding odd-length chunks, and sticking the whole thing inside a FORM chunk.

MIDI Files contain two types of chunks: header chunks and track chunks. A header chunk provides a minimal amount of information pertaining to the entire MIDI file. A track chunk contains a sequential stream of MIDI data which may contain information for up to 16 MIDI channels. The concepts of multiple tracks, multiple MIDI outputs, patterns, sequences, and songs may all be implemented using several track chunks.

A MIDI file always starts with a header chunk, and is followed by one or more track chunks.

```
MThd   <length of header data>
<header data>
MTrk   <length of track data>
<track data>
MTrk   <length of track data>
<track data>
   ...
```

2   Chunk Descriptions

Header Chunks

The header chunk at the beginning of the file specifies some basic information about the data in the file. Here's the syntax of the complete chunk:

```
<Header Chunk> = <chunk type> <length> <format> <ntrks> <division>
```

As described above, <chunk type> is the four ASCII characters 'MThd';
<length> is a 32-bit representation of the number 6 (high byte first).

The data section contains three 16-bit words, stored most-significant byte
first.

The first word, format, specifies the overall organization of the file. Only
three values of format are specified:

   0   the file contains a single multi-channel track

   1   the file contains one or more simultaneous tracks (or MIDI outputs)
       of a sequence

   2   the file contains one or more sequentially independent single-track
       patterns

More information about these formats is provided below.

The next word, ntrks, is the number of track chunks in the file. It will always
be 1 for a format 0 file.

The third word, division, specifies the meaning of the delta-times. It has
two formats, one for metrical time, and one for time-code-based time:

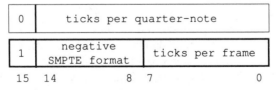

If bit 15 of division is a zero, the bits 14 thru 0 represent the number of delta-
time "ticks" which make up a quarter-note. For instance, if division is 96,
then a time interval of an eighth-note between two events in the file would
be 48.

If bit 15 of division is a one, delta-times in a file correspond to subdivisions of a second, in a way consistent with SMPTE and MIDI time code. Bits 14 thru 8 contain one of the four values -24, -25, -29, or -30, corresponding to the four standard SMPTE and MIDI time code formats (-29 corresponds to 30 drop frame), and represents the number of frames per second. These negative numbers are stored in two's complement form. The second byte (stored positive) is the resolution within a frame: typical values may be 4 (MIDI time code resolution), 8, 10, 80 (bit resolution), or 100. This system allows exact specification of time-code-based tracks, but also allows milli-second-based tracks by specifying 25 frames/sec and a resolution of 40 units per frame. If the events in a file are stored with bit resolution of thirty-frame time code, the division word would be E250 hex.

Formats 0, 1, and 2

A Format 0 file has a header chunk followed by one track chunk. It is the most interchangeable representation of data. It is very useful for a simple single-track player in a program which needs to make synthesizers make sounds, but which is primarily concerned with something else such as mixers or sound effect boxes. It is very desirable to be able to produce such a format, even if your program is track-based, in order to work with these simple programs. On the other hand, perhaps someone will write a format conversion from format 1 to format 0 which might be so easy to use in some setting that it would save you the trouble of putting it into your program.

A Format 1 or 2 file has a header chunk followed by one or more track chunks. Programs which support several simultaneous tracks should be able to save and read data in format 1, a vertically one-dimensional form, that is, as a collection of tracks. Programs which support several independent patterns should be able to save and read data in format 2, a horizontally one-dimensional form. Providing these minimum capabilities will ensure maximum interchangeability.

In a MIDI system with a computer and a SMPTE synchronizer which uses Song Pointer and Timing Clock, tempo maps (which describe the tempo throughout the track, and may also include time signature information, so that the bar number may be derived) are generally created on the computer. To use them with the synchronizer, it is necessary to transfer them from the computer. To make it easy for the synchronizer to extract this data from a MIDI File, tempo information should always be stored in the first MTrk chunk. For a format 0 file, the tempo will be scattered through the track and the tempo map reader should ignore the intervening events; for a format 1 file, the tempo map must be stored as the first track. It is polite to a tempo map reader to offer your user the ability to make a format 0 file with just the tempo, unless you can use format 1.

All MIDI Files should specify tempo and time signature. If they don't, the time signature is assumed to be 4/4, and the tempo 120 beats per minute. In format 0, these meta-events should occur at least at the beginning of the single multi-channel track. In format 1, these meta-events should be contained in the first track. In format 2, each of the temporally independent patterns should contain at least initial time signature and tempo information.

We may decide to define other format IDs to support other structures. A program encountering an unknown format ID may still read other MTrk chunks it finds from the file, as format 1 or 2, if its user can make sense of them and arrange them into some other structure if appropriate. Also, more parameters may be added to the MThd chunk in the future: it is important to read and honor the length, even if it is longer than 6.

Track Chunks

The track chunks (type MTrk) are where actual song data is stored. Each track chunk is simply a stream of MIDI events (and non-MIDI events), preceded by delta-time values. The format for Track Chunks (described below) is exactly the same for all three formats (0, 1, and 2: see "Header Chunk" above) of MIDI Files.

Here is the syntax of an MTrk chunk (the + means "one or more": at least one MTrk event must be present):

```
<Track Chunk> = <chunk type> <length> <MTrk event>+
```

The syntax of an MTrk event is very simple:

```
<MTrk event> = <delta-time> <event>
```

<delta-time> is stored as a variable-length quantity. It represents the amount of time before the following event. If the first event in a track occurs at the very beginning of a track, or if two events occur simultaneously, a delta-time of zero is used. Delta-times are always present. (Not storing delta-times of 0 requires at least two bytes for any other value, and most delta-times aren't zero.) Delta-time is in some fraction of a beat (or a second, for recording a track with SMPTE times), as specified in the header chunk.

```
<event> = <MIDI event> | <sysex event> | <meta-event>
```

<MIDI event> is any MIDI channel message. Running status is used: status bytes of MIDI channel messages may be omitted if the preceding event is a MIDI channel message with the same status. The first event in each MTrk chunk must specify status. Delta-time is not considered an event itself: it is an integral part of the syntax for an MTrk event. Notice that running status occurs across delta-times.

<sysex event> is used to specify a MIDI system exclusive message, either as one unit or in packets, or as an "escape" to specify any arbitrary bytes to be transmitted. A normal complete system exclusive message is stored in a MIDI File in this way:

```
F0 <length> <bytes to be transmitted after F0>
```

The length is stored as a variable-length quantity. It specifies the number of bytes which follow it, not including the F0 or the length itself. For instance, the transmitted message F0 43 12 00 07 F7 would be stored in a MIDI file as F0 05 43 12 00 07 F7. It is required to include the F7 at the end so that the reader of the MIDI file knows that it has read the entire message.

Another form of sysex event is provided which does not imply that an F0 should be transmitted. This may be used as an "escape" to provide for the transmission of things which would not otherwise be legal, including system realtime messages, song pointer or select, MIDI Time Code, etc. This uses the F7 code:

```
F7 <length> <all bytes to be transmitted>
```

Unfortunately, some synthesizer manufacturers specify that their system exclusive messages are to be transmitted as little packets. Each packet is only part of an entire syntactical system exclusive message, but the times they are transmitted at are important. Examples of this are the bytes sent in a CZ patch dump, or the FB-01's "system exclusive mode" in which microtonal data can be transmitted. The F0 and F7 sysex events may be used together to break up syntactically complete system exclusive messages into timed packets.

An F0 sysex event is used for the first packet an a series — it is a message in which the F0 should be transmitted. An F7 sysex event is used for the remainder of the packets, which do not begin with F0. (Of course, the F7 is not considered part of the system exclusive message).

A syntactic system exclusive message must always end with an F7, even if the real-life device didn't send one, so that you know when you've reached the end of an entire sysex message without looking ahead to the next event in the MIDI file. If it's stored in one complete F0 sysex event, the last byte must be an F7. If it is broken up into packets, the last byte of the last packet must be an F7. There also must not be any transmittable MIDI events in between the packets of a multi-packet system exclusive message. This principle is illustrated in the paragraph below.

Here is an example of a multi-packet system exclusive message: suppose the bytes F0 43 12 00 were to be sent, followed by a 200-tick delay, followed by the bytes 43 12 00 43 12 00, followed by a 100-tick delay, followed by the bytes 43 12 00 F7, this would be in the MIDI File:

```
F0 03 43 12 00
81 48                          200-tick delta-time
F7 06 43 12 00 43 12 00
64                             100-tick delta-time
F7 04 43 12 00 F7
```

When reading a MIDI File, and an F7 sysex event is encountered without a preceding F0 sysex event to start a multi-packet system exclusive message sequence, it should be presumed that the F7 event is being used as an "escape". In this case, it is not necessary that it end with an F7, unless it is desired that the F7 be transmitted.

<meta-event> specifies non-MIDI information useful to this format or to sequencers, with this syntax:

```
FF <type> <length> <bytes>
```

All meta-events begin with FF, then have an event type byte (which is always less than 128), and then have the length of the data stored as a variable-length quantity, and then the data itself. If there is no data, the length is 0. As with chunks, future meta-events may be designed which may not be known to existing programs, so programs must properly ignore meta-events which they do not recognize, and indeed, should expect to see them. Programs must never ignore the length of a meta-event which they do recognize, and they shouldn't be surprised if it's bigger than they expected. If so, they must ignore everything past what they know about. However, they must not add anything of their own to the end of a meta-event.

Sysex events and meta-events cancel any running status which was in effect. Running status does not apply to and may not be used for these messages.

3 Meta-Events

A few meta-events are defined herein. It is not required for every program to support every meta-event.

In the syntax descriptions for each of the meta-events a set of conventions is used to describe parameters of the events. The FF which begins each event, the type of each event, and the lengths of events which do not have a variable amount of data are given directly in hexadecimal. A notation such as dd or se, which consists of two lower-case letters, mnemonically represents an 8-bit value. Four identical lower-case letters such as wwww refer to a 16-bit value, stored most-significant-byte first. Six identical lower-case letters such as tttt refer to a 24-bit value, stored most-significant-byte first. The notation len refers to the length portion of the meta-event syntax, that is, a number, stored as a variable-length quantity, which specifies how many data bytes follow it in the meta-event. The notations text and data refer to however many bytes of (possibly text) data were just specified by the length.

In general, meta-events in a track which occur at the same time may occur in any order. If a copyright event is used, it should be placed as early as possible in the file, so it will be noticed easily. Sequence Number and Sequence/Track Name events, if present, must appear at time 0. An end-of-track event must occur as the last event in the track.

Meta-events initially defined include:

FF 00 02 ssss **Sequence Number**

This optional event, which must occur at the beginning of a track, before any nonzero delta-times, and before any transmittable MIDI events, specifies the number of a sequence. In a format 2 MIDI file, it is used to identify each "pattern" so that a "song" sequence using the Cue message to refer to the patterns. If the ID numbers are omitted, the sequences' locations in order in the file are used as defaults. In a format 0 or 1 MIDI file, which only contain one sequence, this number should be contained in the first (or only) track. If transfer of several multitrack sequences is required, this must be done as a group of format 1 files, each with a different sequence number.

`FF 01 len text` **Text Event**
Any amount of text describing anything. It is a good idea to put a text event right at the beginning of a track, with the name of the track, a description of its intended orchestration, and any other information which the user wants to put there. Text events may also occur at other times in a track, to be used as lyrics, or descriptions of cue points. The text in this event should be printable ASCII characters for maximum interchange. However, other character codes using the high-order bit may be used for interchange of files between different programs on the same computer which supports an extended character set. Programs on a computer which does not support non-ASCII characters should ignore those characters.

Meta event types 01 through 0F are reserved for various types of text events, each of which meets the specification of text events(above) but is used for a different purpose:

`FF 02 len text` **Copyright Notice**
Contains a copyright notice as printable ASCII text. The notice should contain the characters (C), the year of the copyright, and the owner of the copyright. If several pieces of music are in the same MIDI file, all of the copyright notices should be placed together in this event so that it will be at the beginning of the file. This event should be the first event in the first track chunk, at time 0.

`FF 03 len text` **Sequence/Track Name**
If in a format 0 track, or the first track in a format 1 file, the name of the sequence. Otherwise, the name of the track.

`FF 04 len text` **Instrument Name**
A description of the type of instrumentation to be used in that track. May be used with the MIDI Prefix meta-event to specify which MIDI channel the description applies to, or the channel may be specified as text in the event itself.

`FF 05 len text` **Lyric**
A lyric to be sung. Generally, each syllable will be a separate lyric event which begins at the event's time.

`FF 06 len text` **Marker**
Normally in a format 0 track, or the first track in a format 1 file. The name of that point in the sequence, such as a rehearsal letter or section name ("First Verse", etc.).

FF 07 len text **Cue Point**
A description of something happening on a film or video screen or stage at that point in the musical score ("Car crashes into house", "curtain opens", "she slaps his face", etc.)

FF 20 01 cc **MIDI Channel Prefix**
The MIDI channel (0-15) contained in this event may be used to associate a MIDI channel with all events which follow, including System Exclusive and meta-events. This channel is "effective" until the next normal MIDI event (which contains a channel) or the next MIDI Channel Prefix meta-event. If MIDI channels refer to "tracks", this message may help jam several tracks into a format 0 file, keeping their non-MIDI data associated with a track. This capability is also present in Yamaha's ESEQ file format.

FF 2F 00 **End of Track**
This event is not optional. It is included so that an exact ending point may be specified for the track, so that it has an exact length, which is necessary for tracks which are looped or concatenated.

FF 51 03 tttttt **Set Tempo, in microseconds/MIDI quarter-note**
This event indicates a tempo change. Another way of putting "microseconds per quarter-note" is "24ths of a microsecond per MIDI clock". Representing tempos as time per beat instead of beat per time allows absolutely exact long-term synchronization with a time-based sync protocol such as SMPTE time code or MIDI time code. This amount of accuracy provided by this tempo resolution allows a four-minute piece at 120 beats per minute to be accurate within 500 usec at the end of the piece. Ideally, these events should only occur where MIDI clocks would be located — this convention is intended to guarantee, or at least increase the likelihood, of compatibility with other synchronization devices so that a time signature/tempo map stored in this format may easily be transferred to another device.

FF 54 05 hr mn se fr ff **SMPTE Offset**
This event, if present, designates the SMPTE time at which the track chunk is supposed to start. It should be present at the beginning of the track, that is, before any nonzero delta-times, and before any transmittable MIDI events. The hour must be encoded with the SMPTE format, just as it is in MIDI Time Code. In a format 1 file, the SMPTE Offset must be stored with the tempo map, and has no meaning in any of the other tracks. The ff field contains fractional frames, in 100ths of a frame, even in SMPTE-based tracks which specify a different frame subdivision for delta-times.

`FF 58 04 nn dd cc bb` **Time Signature**
The time signature is expressed as four numbers. nn and dd represent the numerator and denominator of the time signature as it would be notated. The denominator is a negative power of two: 2 represents a quarter-note, 3 represents an eighth-note, etc. The cc parameter expresses the number of MIDI clocks in a metronome click. The bb parameter expresses the number of notated 32nd-notes in a MIDI quarter-note (24 MIDI Clocks). This was added because there are already multiple programs which allow the user to specify that what MIDI thinks of as a quarter-note (24 clocks) is to be notated as, or related to in terms of, something else.

Therefore, the complete event for 6/8 time, where the metronome clicks every three eighth-notes, but there are 24 clocks per quarter-note, 72 to the bar, would be (in hex):

`FF 58 04 06 03 24 08`

That is, 6/8 time (8 is 2 to the 3rd power, so this is 06 03), 36 MIDI clocks per dotted-quarter (24 hex!), and eight notated 32nd-notes per MIDI quarter note.

```
FF 59 02 sf mi  Key Signature
  sf = -7: 7 flats
  sf = -1: 1 flat
  sf = 0: key of C
          sf=1:  1 sharp

  sf = 7: 7 sharps
  mi = 0: major key
  mi = 1: minor key
```

`FF 7F len data` **Sequencer-Specific Meta-Event**
Special requirements for particular sequencers may use this event type: the first byte or bytes of data is a manufacturer ID (these are one byte, or, if the first byte is 00, three bytes). As with MIDI System Exclusive, manufacturers who define something using this meta-event should publish it so that others may know how to use it. After all, this is an interchange format. This type of event may be used by a sequencer which elects to use this as its only file format; sequencers with their established feature-specific formats should probably stick to the standard features when using this format.

4 Program Fragments and Example MIDI Files

Here are some of the routines to read and write variable-length numbers in
MIDI Files. These routines are in C, and use getc and putc, which read and
write single 8-bit characters from/to the files infile and outfile.

```
WriteVarLen (value)
register long value;
{
  register long buffer;

  buffer = value & 0x7f;
  while ((value >>= 7) > 0)
  {
    buffer <<= 8;
    buffer |= 0x80;
    buffer += (value & 0x7f);
  }
  while (TRUE)
  {
    putc(buffer,outfile);
    if (buffer & 0x80)
      buffer >>= 8;
    else
      break;
  }
}


doubleword ReadVarLen ()
{
  register doubleword value;
  register byte c;
  if ((value = getc(infile)) & 0x80)
  {
    value &= 0x7f;
    do
    {
      value = (value << 7) + ((c = getc(infile)) & 0x7f);
    } while (c & 0x80);
  }
  return (value);
}
```

As an example, MIDI Files for the following excerpt are shown below. First, a format 0 file is shown, with all information intermingled; then, a format 1 file is shown with all data separated into four tracks: one for tempo and time signature, and three for the notes. A resolution of 96 "ticks" per quarter note is used. A time signature of 4/4 and a tempo of 120, though implied, are explicitly stated.

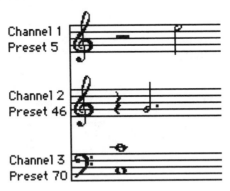

The contents of the MIDI stream represented by this example are broken down here:

Delta Time (decimal)	Event Code (hex)	Other Bytes (decimal)	Comment
0	FF 58	04 04 02 24 08	4 bytes: 4/4 time, 24 MIDI clocks/click, 8 32nd notes/24 MIDI clocks
0	FF 51	03 500000	3 bytes: 500,000 μsec per quarter-note
0	C0	5	Ch. 1, Program Change 5
0	C1	46	Ch. 2, Program Change 46
0	C2	70	Ch. 3, Program Change 70
0	92	48 96	Ch. 3 Note On C2, forte
0	92	60 96	Ch. 3 Note On C3, forte
96	91	67 64	Ch. 2 Note On G3, mezzo-forte
96	90	76 32	Ch. 1 Note On E4, piano
192	82	48 64	Ch. 3 Note Off C2, standard
0	82	60 64	Ch. 3 Note Off C3, standard
0	81	67 64	Ch. 2 Note Off G3, standard
0	80	76 64	Ch. 1 Note Off E4, standard
0	FF 2F	00	Track End

The entire format 0 MIDI file contents in hex follow. First, the header chunk:

```
4D 54 68 64              MThd
00 00 00 06              chunk length
00 00                    format 0
00 01                    one track
00 60                    96 per quarter-note
```

Then, the track chunk. Its header, followed by the events (notice that running status is used in places):

```
4D 54 72 6B              MTrk
00 00 00 3B              chunk length (59)
```

Delta-time	Event	Comments
00	FF 58 04 04 02 18 08	time signature
00	FF 51 03 07 A1 20	tempo
00	C0 05	
00	C1 2E	
00	C2 46	
00	92 30 60	
00	3C 60	running status
60	91 43 40	
60	90 4C 20	
81 40	82 30 40	two-byte delta-time
00	3C 40	running status
00	81 43 40	
00	80 4C 40	
00	FF 2F 00	end of track

A format 1 representation of the file is slightly different. Its header chunk:

```
4D 54 68 64              MThd
00 00 00 06              chunk length
00 01                    format
00 04                    four tracks
00 60                    96 per quarter-note
```

First, the track chunk for the time signature/tempo track. Its header, followed by the events:

```
4D 54 72 6B              MTrk
00 00 00 14              chunk length (20)
```

Delta-time	Event	Comments
00	FF 58 04 04 02 18 08	time signature
00	FF 51 03 07 A1 20	tempo
83 00	FF 2F 00	end of track

Then, the track chunk for the first music track. The MIDI convention for note on/off running status is used in this example:

4D 54 72 6B	MTrk
00 00 00 10	chunk length (16)

Delta-time	Event	Comments
00	C0 05	
81 40	90 4C 20	
81 40	4C 00	Running status:note on,vel=0
00	FF 2F 00	end of track

Then, the track chunk for the second music track:

4D 54 72 6B	MTrk
00 00 00 0F	chunk length (15)

Delta-time	Event	Comments
00	C1 2E	
60	91 43 40	
82 20	43 00	running status
00	FF 2F 00	end of track

Then, the track chunk for the third music track:

4D 54 72 6B	MTrk
00 00 00 15	chunk length (21)

Delta-time	Event	Comments
00	C2 46	
00	92 30 60	
00	3C 60	running status
83 00	30 00	two-byte delta-time, running status
00	3C 00	running status
00	FF 2F 00	end of track

Part Four

Writing MIDI Software

Part Four

Writing MIDI Software

Wading in the MIDI Data Stream

Virtually any program designed to process MIDI data in real-time can be structured around the following four steps.

1. Get a byte from the MIDI In port.
2. Parse the byte.
3. Process the byte.
4. Send the processed byte to the MIDI Out port.

The first and last steps are simple enough, each requiring a single program statement. These two steps are the only ones that actually access the MIDI buffers. In our examples we will reference the routine ReadMIDI whenever we want to get a byte from the MIDI input buffer, and WriteMIDI whenever we want to send a byte to the MIDI output buffer. The actual code for these two simple routines is dependent on the particular computer and computer/MIDI interface hardware used. You may choose to access your computer's serial ports with your own assembly language driver, use commands from one of the commercially available sets of MIDI programming tools, or use device-specific code to access data from a "smart" interface, such as the Roland MPU-401, or IBM MIDI Card.

The second and third steps involve several levels of code. The routines called in these steps are where all of the actual parsing and processing take place. These steps will require little, if any, MIDI-specific code or hardware. They can be written in machine code, Pascal "C," or any high level language. We'll develop our examples using Pascal.

Ripples in the Data Stream

Before we get into the code examples, we need to look more closely into the flow of MIDI data. MIDI processing would be pretty simple if all messages were sent using the normal transmission format with each MIDI message sent in its entirety, starting with the status byte, followed by all associated data bytes in their proper order. If this general rule were strictly adhered to by all devices, the MIDI data stream would be smooth and fairly predictable, making it easy to parse. However, in order to minimize the time it takes to transmit long strings of Channel messages, and in order to optimize synchronization accuracy, there are two exceptions to this general rule. These exceptions are: Running Status format transmission, and prioritized System Real-Time messages. These exceptions help to make MIDI such a powerful medium, but they also introduce some ripples in the MIDI data stream.

Running Status Format

As described previously, Running Status format is a time-saving method for transmitting long strings of Channel messages of the same status without sending redundant status bytes. Running Status is cancelled by the reception of any new status byte — with one exception. System Real-Time messages can be inserted anywhere within a string of Running Status bytes and their arrival can temporarily interrupt Running Status. Note that, although this method is optional for transmitters, all receivers (and that includes your programs) must be able to handle Running Status format.

Prioritized System Real-Time Messages

System Real-Time messages have priority over all other types of MIDI messages. These single-byte messages are used to sycnchronize devices in a MIDI system. In order to maintain the most accurate synchronization possible, these messages can be inserted anywhere within the MIDI data stream. They can be sent within a string of Running Status bytes, or even between the bytes of other messages.

Guidelines for Parsing the MIDI Data Stream

A MIDI program, like any MIDI receiver, must be able to parse messages received in normal and Running Status formats, as well as prioritized transmission of System Real-Time messages. Here are some guidlelines for creating your own parsing routines.

- Every incoming byte must be identified as either a MIDI status byte or a data byte.

- Use a status buffer variable to hold the value of the last received Channel Voice or Channel Mode status byte, with these exceptions:

  The buffer should be cleared on start-up, or whenever a System Common, System Exclusive, or ignored Channel message status is received.

  The buffer should be left unaltered whenever any System Real-Time Message is received.

- The parsing routine can use the value of the status buffer to select the appropriate message processing routines.

- The program should ignore all incoming bytes while the status buffer value is zero.

- Use a counter variable to keep track of the order of received bytes. It should be cleared whenever a new, recognized status is received. It should be incremented by one each time a subsequent data byte is received, starting with the first data byte, and set to 1 when the final byte of the message is received. The counter should not be altered if a System Real-Time status byte is received.

- Processing routines for each recognized message can use the counter value to determine which byte of a message they are currently processing.

Parsing by Value

		HEX	DECIMAL	DESCRIPTION
DATA		00–7F	0–127	MIDI DATA
CHANNEL STATUS BYTES		80–8F	128–143	NOTE OFF
		90–9F	144–159	NOTE ON
		A0–AF	160–175	POLY KEY PRESSURE
		B0–BF	176–191	CONTROL CHANGE
		C0–CF	192–207	PROGRAM CHANGE
		D0–DF	208–223	CHANNEL PRESSURE
		E0–EF	224–239	PITCH WHEEL CHANGE
SYSTEM COMMON STATUS BYTES		F0	240	SYSTEM EXCLUSIVE
		F1	241	MTC QUARTER FRAME
		F2	242	SONG POSITION POINTER
		F3	243	SONG SELECT
		F4	244	UNDEFINED
		F5	245	UNDEFINED
		F6	246	TUNE REQUEST
		F7	247	END OF EXCLUSIVE
SYSTEM REAL TIME STATUS BYTES		F8	248	MIDI CLOCK
		F9	249	UNDEFINED
		FA	250	START
		FB	251	CONTINUE
		FC	252	STOP
		FD	253	UNDEFINED
		FE	254	ACTIVE SENSING
		FF	255	SYSTEM RESET

Once a byte has been retrieved from the MIDI In buffer it must be parsed, or separated into component parts. In terms of the MIDI data stream, incoming bytes can be separated into two types: status or data. This is simple enough to do, since bit 7 is set to 1 in any status byte and set to 0 in any data byte. Bytes with a value equal to or greater than 128 (80H) are status bytes. Bytes with a value equal to or less than 127 (7FH) are data bytes. A simple comparison test will separate status bytes from data bytes. Here is an outline for a process to check each incoming byte and identify it as a status or data byte.

Get a byte from the MIDI In port.

If the byte is equal to or greater than 80H, it is a status byte.

If the byte is equal to or less than 7FH, it is a data byte

When a status byte is detected, it's generally a good idea to determine the type of message: Channel, System Common, System Exclusive, or System Real-Time, since each of these requires different processing. When Channel messages are received, the program must be prepared to handle Running Status format. This means that the status buffer and byte count will have to be updated. When System Common or System Exclusive messages are received, the status buffer and byte counter should be cleared. (For now, we'll ignore these messages.) When System Real-Time messages are received, the status buffer and byte counter should not be changed at all. If the program recognizes System Real Time messages, the message should be processed immediately.

When a status byte is received, you can determine the type of message by comparing its value with the range of values for each message type. When a data byte is received, it is processed according to the value of the last received status byte and by determining its order in the message. (Is it the first data byte since the status byte was received? — the second?, etc.)

An outline for a procedure to follow when a new status byte is detected is shown below. This outline shows how to determine the message type as well as how to handle the status buffer and counter appropriately for each type.

    Update status buffer:
        If byte = 80-EFH, byte is Channel message status
            set status buffer to value of the byte
            clear counter

        If byte = F0- F7H, byte is System Common
            clear status buffer (to ignore these messages for now)
            clear counter

        If byte = F8H-FFH, byte is System Real-Time
            don't change status buffer (interrupt Running Status)
            process System Real-Time if recognized

When the status byte is received, the status buffer is assigned its value (if it is recognized by the program). The status buffer is cleared if the status is not recognized. If a System Real-Time status is received, the status buffer is not changed (whether the program recognizes System Real-Time or not). The value of the status buffer is then used to process all incoming bytes. If the status buffer value has been cleared, all subsequent data bytes will be ignored. (The program does nothing with them beyond parsing them as data.) If the status buffer is not zero, its value is used to parse data bytes to the appropriate processing routine. An outline for parsing based on the value of the status buffer is shown below.

Parse byte based on value of status buffer:

If status buffer = 0, do nothing (bytes are for unrecognized message)

If status buffer = 80H-9FH, call routine to process Note On/Off message

If status buffer = A0H-AFH, call routine to process P Pressure message

If status buffer = B0H-BFH, call routine to process C Change message

If status buffer = C0H-CFH, call routine to process P Change message

If status buffer = D0H-DFH, call routine to process C Pressure message

If status buffer = E0H-EFH, call routine to process P Wheel message

Parsing by Order

	STATUS BYTE	DATA BYTE 1	DATA BYTE 2
CHANNEL STATUS BYTES	NOTE OFF	NOTE NUMBER	RELEASE VELOCITY
	NOTE ON	NOTE NUMBER	ATTACK VELOCITY
	POLY KEY PRESSURE	NOTE NUMBER	PRESSURE VALUE
	CONTROL CHANGE	CONTROLLER ID	CONTROLLER VALUE
	PROGRAM CHANGE	PROGRAM NUMBER	-
	CHANNEL PRESSURE	PRESSURE VALUE	-
	PITCH WHEEL CHANGE	PITCH BEND LSB	PITCH WHEEL MSB
SYSTEM COMMON STATUS BYTES	SYSTEM EXCLUSIVE	ID NUMBER	*
	MTC QUARTER FRAME	MESSAGE NUMBER	-
	SONG POSITION POINTER	SONG POSITION LSB	SONG POSITION MSB
	SONG SELECT	SONG ID NUMBER	-
	UNDEFINED	-	-
	UNDEFINED	-	-
	TUNE REQUEST	-	-
	END OF EXCLUSIVE	-	-
SYSTEM REAL TIME STATUS BYTES	MIDI CLOCK	-	-
	UNDEFINED	-	-
	START	-	-
	CONTINUE	-	-
	STOP	-	-
	UNDEFINED	-	-
	ACTIVE SENSING	-	-
	SYSTEM RESET	-	-

* ANY NUMBER OF DATA BYTES MAY FOLLOW, DEPENDING ON THE SPECIFIC SYSEX MESSAGE

In order to process any MIDI message, you need to know two things: the type of MIDI message, and which byte in the message to process. As we've seen, you can determine the status type by comparing the value of the byte to status values defined in the MIDI specification. Once you know the status type, you will know the number of bytes in the message. For example, Note On and Note Off messages are three bytes, Program Change messages are two bytes, and all System Real-Time messages are single-byte. (See the table on the preceding page.) Your MIDI programs must have some mechanism to keep track of the byte count of incoming messages. This makes it possible to parse bytes by their order in a message. Suppose, for instance, you want to process Note On and Note Off messages. The message is made up of three bytes: status byte, key number (data byte 1), and velocity value (data byte 2). Depending on whether you want to process the note's channel, pitch, or velocity, you may want to alter the value of the first, second, or third byte of the message (or any combination of the three).

		IF COUNTER VALUE IS:	PROCESS THIS BYTE	THEN RESET COUNTER TO:
NEW STATUS RESETS COUNTER TO ZERO → CHANNEL VOICE STATUS	NOTE ON	0	NOTE ON STATUS	COUNTER +1
DATA	NOTE NUMBER	1	NOTE NUMBER	COUNTER +1
DATA	VELOCITY VALUE	2	VELOCITY VALUE	COUNTER = 1
DATA	NOTE NUMBER	1	NOTE NUMBER	COUNTER +1
NEW STATUS RESETS COUNTER TO ZERO → DATA	VELOCITY VALUE	2	VELOCITY VALUE	COUNTER = 1
CHANNEL VOICE STATUS	CONTROL CHANGE	0	C. CHANGE STATUS	COUNTER +1
DATA	CONTROL ID	1	CONTROL ID	COUNTER +1
DATA	CONTROL VALUE	2	CONTROL VALUE	COUNTER = 1

One simple way to keep track of the byte count is to set up a variable to count the bytes of a message as they arrive. Whenever a new status byte is received, the counter is cleared (set to zero). When the first data byte arrives, the counter is incremented to 1. When the second data byte arrives, the counter is incremented to 2, and so on. When the last byte of a Channel message is received, the counter is set to 1. This leaves you ready to handle the next byte if it's sent under Running Status (in which case, the byte will be the first data byte of a new message of the same status). Your processing routine can check the value of the counter to determine which byte it is operating on. Following is an outline based on the previous examples which shows how bytes of a Note On message would be parsed. Note that the counter is cleared whenever a new status byte is received, set to 1 whenever the last byte of a message is received, and not altered when System Real-Time messages are received. This makes it possible to keep track of byte order if Running Status format is used, or if prioritized System Real-Time messages are received.

Note On (90H) status byte received, followed by note number and velocity data bytes:

Update status buffer:
    If byte = 80-EFH, byte is Channel message status
        set status buffer to value of the byte (buffer is set to 90H)
        clear counter
    If byte = F0- F7H, byte is System Common
        clear status buffer (to ignore these mesages for now)
        clear counter
    If byte = F8H-FFH, byte is System Real-Time
        don't change status buffer (interrupt Running Status)
        process System Real-Time if recognized

Parse byte based on value of status buffer:
    If status buffer = 80H-9FH, call routine to process Note On/Off message

Process Note On/Off :
        If counter = 0:
            process Note On status byte
            increment counter
        If counter = 1:
            process key number byte
            increment counter
        If counter = 2:
            process velocity value data byte
            set counter to 1

Real-Time MIDI Processing Shell

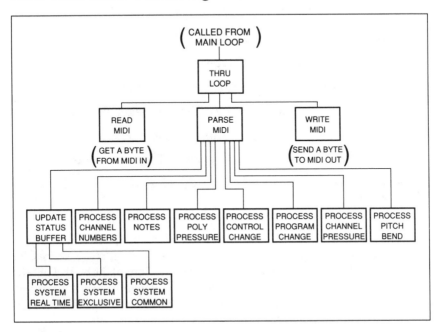

The following code examples make up a shell for the real-time processing portion of a generic MIDI Thru application. The examples in this book will not cover any aspect of the program's user interface*, other than to demonstrate how to access variables that would be set in run-time by the user. For example, we'll show you how to select any type of message for processing. It's up to you to design the code that lets the user specify (whether by mouse click, menu selection, or whatever) which messages to process or ignore.

*If you'd like to learn more about the user-interface aspects of MIDI programming, we recommend our book, *MIDI Programming for the Macintosh*, and also *MIDI Programming in "C"*, by Jim Conger. Both are available from M&T Books, 501 Galveston Drive, Redwood City CA. 94063

The design of the shell is based on the previous outlines and demonstrates how to perform the following tasks.

- Get incoming MIDI data from the MIDI input buffer
- Parse the data by message type
- Handle Running Status format reception properly
- Handle prioritized System Real Time messages properly
- Pass recognized messages to appropriate processing routines
- Send the processed messages to the MIDI output buffer
- Ignore selected messages (Don't process or send to the output buffer.)

In the initial example, only Channel message are recognized. This will allow us to focus on the overall structure of the shell. (We'll cover processing routines for all message types in the following sections of the book. For now, we've included comments in the code to point out where the calls to various processing routines would be inserted.) All System messages are ignored, and are not sent to the MIDI Out port.

Constants and Variables

First things first. Before we can go any further, we should create a list of constants and variables for our routines to use. At this point, we'll need constants for the various status types, and a few variables — one to hold the MIDI byte, one for the status buffer, and one for the counter. We'll also declare a flag variable that would be used to turn on and off the MIDI Thru loop.

```
CONST
{range limits for each status type}
  NoteOff1 = $80;          {NoteOff/Channel 1}
  NoteOff16 = $8F;         {NoteOff/Channel 16}
  NoteOn1 = $90;           {etc. ....}
  NoteOn16 = $9F;
  PolyPress1 = $A0;
  PolyPress16 = $AF;
  ControlChange1 = $B0;
  ControlChange16 = $BF;
  ProgramChange1 = $C0;
  ProgramChange16 = $CF;
  ChanPress1 = $D0;
  ChanPress16 = $DF;
  PitchWheel1 = $E0;
  PitchWheel16 = $EF;
  TimingClock = $F8;
  SystemReset = $FF;
  SysEx = $F0;             {lowest System Common status value}
  QFrame = $F1;            {MTC Quarter Frame Message}
  EOX = $F7;               {highest System Common status value}


VAR
  theMIDIByte: Integer;  {byte received from your MIDI In routine}
  statusBuffer: Integer; {used to hold last received status value}
  dataCount: Integer;    {counts the order of data bytes received}
  ThruFlag: Boolean;     {used to turn Thru Loop On/Off}
```

MIDI Thru Loop

The highest level procedure of the shell is the procedure ThruLoop. This procedure handles the basic MIDI Thru algorithm: Get a byte, parse the byte, process the byte, and send the byte to the MIDI Out port. It would be called from within the main program loop. ThruLoop executes repeatedly as long as the ThruFlag is on. (The value of this flag would be under user control. For example, a menu selection or mouse click might be used to turn it off.) There are only three steps in the loop. First, a byte is retrieved from the MIDI In port. Then the ParseMIDI routine is called to determine what kind of byte it is and, if appropriate, to process it. Finally, the byte is sent to the MIDI Out port. Note that the byte is not sent if the status buffer has been cleared (statusBuffer := Ignore).

```
PROCEDURE ThruLoop;
BEGIN
  WHILE ThruFlag DO
  BEGIN
    ReadMIDI(theMIDIByte);
    ParseMIDI;
    IF statusBuffer <> Ignore THEN
      WriteMIDI(theMIDIByte);
  END; {WHILE TRUE}
END; {ThruLoop}
```

The ReadMIDI and WriteMIDI procedure shells should be replaced with the specific code that reads and writes a byte from and to your computer/ MIDI interface.

```
PROCEDURE ReadMIDI (theMIDIbyte: integer);
BEGIN
  ;{use any routine that returns a MIDI Byte from MIDI In}
END;{ReadMIDI}

PROCEDURE WriteMIDI (theMIDIbyte: integer);
BEGIN
  ;{use any routine that sends a MIDI Byte to MIDI Out}
END;{WriteMIDI}
```

Parsing Procedures

ParseMIDI is called whenever a new byte is received from the MIDI In port. It is used to parse all incoming bytes and, when appropriate, to call routines to process them. It is divided into two blocks. In the first block, each incoming byte is checked to see if it is a status or a data byte. In the second block, the byte is parsed by message type and processed.

When a status byte is detected in the first block, depending on the status type, the following should take place:

- Channel : Set the status buffer to the new status. Clear the counter.

- System Exclusive: Clear the status buffer and counter. (For now, we won't recognize these messages.)

- System Common: Clear the status buffer and counter. (For now, we won't recognize these messages.)

- System Real-Time: Do not change the status buffer or counter. (This will make it possible for these messages to interrupt other messages.) The routine to handle System Real-Time messages would be called at this point, since they should be processed as soon as they are received. Once the message is processed, get the next byte from MIDI In and start all over again.

Rather than include the code for all of those possibilities inside ParseMIDI, we simply call another routine, UpdateStatus, to handle the details. Once these initial tasks are done, a case-structure is used to parse the MIDI byte according to the current status buffer value. A separate case-statement is used for each recognized message type. The value of the status buffer is used as the selection variable of the case-structure. (Its value was previously set by UpdateStatus.) If its value is zero, the Ignore case-statement is executed. This is an empty block. No processing of the byte is performed (which is what "ignore" means in terms of our example application). This happens whenever the last received status byte was a type not recognized by the program. If the value of the status buffer is not zero, it is the value of the last received recognized status. The case-statement corresponding to its value is executed. Each case-statement consists of a call to a routine that handles processing of that specific message type. For example, if a Note On status is received, the NoteOff1..NoteOn16 case-statement is executed. When the data bytes for the Note On message arrive, they are trapped at the same case-statement and routed to the same processing routine. The processing routine uses the counter value to determine which byte in the message it is processing. Comments show where the calls to the processing routines would go. We'll fill in the details later on.

```
PROCEDURE ParseMIDI;
BEGIN

{Parse status/data and process System Messages}
   IF theMIDIByte >= NoteOff1 THEN     {parse status bytes}
     UpdateStatus;                   {update buffer if necessary}

{Parse Channel Message bytes and process recognized messages}
   CASE statusBuffer OF   {process byte based on status}
     Ignore:
       ; {do nothing with unrecognized status or data bytes}

   {call processing routines for recognized status types here}
     NoteOff1..NoteOn16:
         ; {Call Note processing routine}

     PolyPress1..PolyPress16:
         ;{Call Poly Pressure processing routine}

     ControlChange1..ControlChange16:
         ;{Call Control Change processing routine}

     ProgramChange1..ProgramChange16:
         ;{Call Program Change processing routine}

     ChanPress1..ChanPress16:
         ;{Call Channel Pressure processing routine}

     PitchWheel1..PitchWheel16:
         ;{Call Pitch Wheel processing routine}

     OTHERWISE
       ; {bytes belong to unrecognized status, do nothing}
   END;{CASE statusBuffer}
 END; {ParseMIDI}
```

Whenever a new status byte is detected by ParseMIDI, UpdateStatus is called. It uses a case structure to parse the status byte as a Channel, System Exclusive, System Common, or System Real-Time message. When a Channel message status byte is received, the status buffer is assigned the value of the byte and the counter is cleared. At that point, control returns to ParseMIDI and the Channel byte is handled according to its status. All subsequent data bytes will be processed under the same status, so Running Status format messages will be handled correctly.

When a System Exclusive message status byte is received, the status buffer is cleared and the counter is set to zero. Control returns to ParseMIDI and, since the status buffer value is zero, any subsequent data bytes are ignored. These messages, when recognized, require different parsing techniques than those used for Channel messages. We would process them here before returning to ParseMIDI. (See *Processing System Exclusive Messages* .)

When a System Common message status byte is received, the status buffer is cleared and the counter is set to zero. Control returns to ParseMIDI and, since the status buffer value is zero, any subsequent data bytes are ignored. If we were looking for MTC Quarter-Frame messages, we would process these messages here before returning to ParseMIDI. Processing them as soon as they arrive helps to maintain synchronization accuracy. If MTC synchronization is not a factor in the application, System Common messages could either be handled here, or after returning to ParseMIDI. In the latter case, you would set the status buffer to the value of the received System Common status byte in UpdateStatus, and add a System Common case-statement to ParseMIDI.

When a System Real-Time message status byte is received (and your application recognizes it), the message is processed immediately. Since the status buffer and counter values should never be changed when a System Real-Time message is received, it is necessary to get the next MIDI byte before returning to ParseMIDI. (Otherwise, ParseMIDI would attempt to process the System Real-Time byte as a data byte of another status!) There is no way to predict whether the next byte will be a status or a data byte so, after the byte is received, UpdateStatus is called again (a recursive procedure call). Once the new byte has been checked by Update status, control returns to ParseMIDI.

```
PROCEDURE  UpdateStatus;
BEGIN
  CASE theMIDIByte OF

    NoteOff1..PitchWheel16:{range of all Channel status messages}
    BEGIN
      statusBuffer := theMIDIByte;{assign this status to statusBuffer }
      dataCount := 0;              {new status, reset value of dataCount}
    END;

    SysEX:  {SysEx messages will processed from here}
    BEGIN
      statusBuffer := Ignore;{ignore these messages for now}
      dataCount := 0;              {new status, reset value of dataCount}
    END;

    QFrame..EOX: {range of all System Common messages}
    BEGIN
      statusBuffer := Ignore;    {ignore these messages for now}
      dataCount := 0;              {new status, reset value of dataCount}
    END;

    OTHERWISE {theMIDIByte must be a Real-Time status byte}
    BEGIN
      ; {process System Real-Time bytes here}
      ReadMIDI(theMIDIByte);    {get the next byte}
      IF theMIDIByte >= NoteOff1 THEN
        UpdateStatus;            {if it's a status byte update buffer}
    END;
  END; {CASE theMIDIByte}
END;  {UpdateStatusBuffer}
```

Processing Channel Voice Messages

Now that we have a shell that can parse incoming MIDI data in real-time, we can look at ways to modify it to process the different types of Channel Voice messages. The parsing routines handle normal or Running Status formats, as well as prioritized System Real-Time messages in a way that is transparent to the processing routines. We no longer have to be concerned about those ripples in the data stream and can concentrate on how we want to process the different Channel Voice messages. The following list gives some of the effects produced by processing Channel Voice messages.

- Turn reception of messages from a given channel on or off
- Turn reception of messages of a given type on or off
- Turn reception of messages of a given type on or off for a given channel
- Reassign messages from a given channel to any other channel
- Shift selected channel numbers by a given offset
- Reassign a given program number to any other program number.
- Ignore program numbers beyond a certain range
- Shift a range of program numbers. For example, shift numbers 33-64 to numbers 1-32
- Reassign a given controller ID to any other controller ID
- Customize controller effects with various curves: inverse, log, anti-log, offset, shelf, etc.
- Transpose a given range of notes by a given interval
- Reassign a given note to any other note
- Invert the note order of a keyboard or controller
- Customize velocity effects with various curves: inverse, log, anti-log, offset, shelf, etc.
- Customize pressure effects with various curves: inverse, log, anti-log, offset, shelf, etc.

It might surprise you to learn that all of these effects can be installed in the shell with routines that are based on two simple processing algorithims — filters and mappers. Filters are used to selectively turn something on or off; mappers are used to reassign values.

Filters

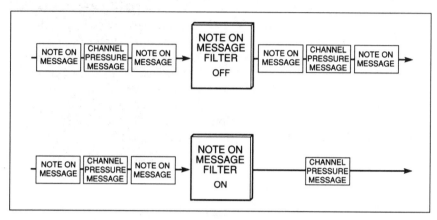

These are routines that allow the program to selectively ignore bytes in a given range of values. Filter routines are typically used to enable/disable recognition of different types of messages or to enable/disable recognition of messages on any given channel. (In MIDI Thru applications, these messages would go in but not out, and, therefore, never get to any devices attached to the application's MIDI Thru port.) The following examples show how to revise the MIDI Thru shell to add features that can remove messages of any type, or remove messages on any channel from the MIDI data stream.

Message Filters

Here's an example of how to modify the previous code examples to add the ability to filter out any type of Channel message. First, create a set of on/off flags — one for each Channel message. (Allow the user to select the filter effect when the program is running by turning the flag on or off via menu selection, mouse click, or other input method.)

```
CONST
  FilterOn = False;              {filter is on don't pass data}
  FilterOff = True;              {filter is off process and pass data}

VAR
  NoteFlag: Boolean;        {used to turn processing routines on/off for}
  PPressFlag: Boolean;      {each of the different message types}
  CCHangeFlag: Boolean;
  PChangeFlag: Boolean;
  CPressFlag: Boolean;
  PWheelFlag: Boolean;
```

Insert a test for each flag in the parsing routine's case-statments. The test is placed immediately before the code that calls the processing routine. If the filter flag has been set to "FilterOn," process the data as usual. If the filter flag is set to "FilterOff," skip the processing step and clear the status buffer and counter variables. Now it is possible to turn on or off the reception of any Channel message. Here's how ParseMIDI looks with the tests inserted.

```
PROCEDURE ParseMIDI;
 BEGIN
{Parse status/data and process System Messages}
   IF theMIDIByte >= NoteOff1 THEN{parse status bytes from data bytes}
   BEGIN
     UpdateStatus;                          {update buffer if necessary}

{Parse Channel Message bytes and process recognized messages}
   CASE statusBuffer OF                 {process byte based on status}
     Ignore:
       ; {do nothing with unrecognized status or data bytes}
  {call processing routines for recognized status types}

     NoteOff1..NoteOn16:
       IF NoteFlag THEN
   {Call Note processing routine}
       ELSE
       BEGIN
         statusBuffer := Ignore;
         dataCount := 0;
       END; {Call Note processing routine}

     PolyPress1..PolyPress16:
       IF PPressFlag THEN
   {Call Poly Pressure processing routine}
       ELSE
       BEGIN
         statusBuffer := Ignore;
         dataCount := 0;
       END;

     ControlChange1..ControlChange16:
       IF CChangeFlag THEN
   {Call Control Change processing routine}
       ELSE
       BEGIN
         statusBuffer := Ignore;
         dataCount := 0;
       END;
```

```
  ProgramChange1..ProgramChange16:
    IF PChangeFlag THEN
{Call P Change processing routine}
    ELSE
    BEGIN
      statusBuffer := Ignore;
      dataCount := 0;
    END;

  ChanPress1..ChanPress16:
    IF CPressFlag THEN
{Call Channel Pressure processing routine}
    ELSE
    BEGIN
      statusBuffer := Ignore;
      dataCount := 0;
    END;

  PitchWheel1..PitchWheel16:
    IF PWheelFlag THEN
{Call P Wheel processing routine}
    ELSE
    BEGIN
      statusBuffer := Ignore;
      dataCount := 0;
    END;

  OTHERWISE
    ; {bytes belong to unrecognized status, do nothing}
  END;{CASE statusBuffer}
END; {ParseMIDI}
```

Channel Filters

It is often useful to selectively filter out messages on a specific channel (or channels) from incoming MIDI data. The first step required is to get a "hit-list" of channels to be filtered out from the user. To enable the filtering, each incoming Channel message status byte must be trapped and its channel number read. If the channel number is on the hit-list, the program should clear the status buffer. (Remember, while the status buffer value is cleared, all incoming bytes are ignored, i.e filtered out.)

Adding channel filters to the example code simply requires adding a channel flag to the variable list. It is used to select channel processing.

```
VAR
  ChannelFlag: Boolean;  {used to turn Channel processing on/off}
```

The hit-list will be stored as a 16-element array, Channel [n], which indicates which channel numbers to filter out. The array is indexed from 0-15. The index value corresponds to the channel number. The element value will indicate whether or not the channel number is filtered. We'll use "-1" to indicate that a channel should be filtered. MIDI Channels 1-16 are encoded as data values 0-15 (data value 0=MIDI Channel 1, data value 1=MIDI Channel 2, etc. For example Channel[0]=-1, means filter out messages on channel 1. Channel[15]=-1, means filter out messages on channel 16. (Allow the user to select channels by altering this array when the program is running.

```
VAR
  Channel: ARRAY[0..15] OF integer;
```

The status byte's channel number is used to point to the appropriate element in the channel array, so we'll need a way to get the channel number from a given status byte. The channel number is held in the low-order four bits of a Channel message status byte. To extract a channel number from a status byte, "AND" the status byte with the masking constant 0FH. The returned value will have the channel number on the lower four bits. The higher four bits will be cleared. Here is a function that is passed a status byte value and returns the channel number.

```
FUNCTION GetChannel (byte: integer): integer;
  VAR
    X: integer;
BEGIN
  X := BitAND(byte, $F);
  GetChannel := X;
END;{GetChannel}
```

To trap incoming Channel status bytes, each byte is tested to see if it is within the range of Channel status bytes "AND" the channel filter flag is on. If so, ProcessChannels is called to check the channel number against the hit-list stored in the channel array. A single IF statement performs the test. It is inserted in ParseMIDI right after the call to UpdateStatus:

```
 PROCEDURE ParseMIDI;
 BEGIN
{Parse status/data and process System Messages}
   IF theMIDIByte >= NoteOff1 THEN{parse status bytes from data bytes}
   BEGIN
     UpdateStatus;          {update buffer if necessary}
     IF (theMIDIByte < SysEx) AND (ChannelFlag) THEN
       ProcessChannels;    {Call Channel processing routine}
   END;
   .  .  .
   .  .  .
 END;{ParseMIDI}
```

In the channel processing procedure, we need to look at the channel number of the status byte and compare it with the array element with the same index number. If the element of that value is -1, the procedure should clear the status buffer. This will cause the message to be ignored. The previously described GetChannel function is used to return the byte's channel value.

```
 PROCEDURE ProcessChannels;
   VAR
     channelNumber: integer;
 BEGIN
   channelNumber := GetChannel(theMIDIByte);
   IF Channel[channelNumber] = -1 THEN
     statusBuffer := ignore;
 END;{ProcessChannels}
```

Mappers

These are routines that reassign the value of a byte by using its original value as a pointer to a new value. Some ways to use mapping algorithms are listed below.

- Reassign program numbers

- Reassign channel numbers

- Reassign note numbers to create transposition or harmony zones

- Reassign controller ID numbers

- Scale velocity data to any curve (inverse, log, anti-log, etc.)

- Scale controller data to any curve (inverse, log, anti-log, etc.)

One way to set up a mapping algorithm for a particular data type (such as channel number or velocity value) is to create an array with an equal number of elements and data values. (A channel mapping array has 16 elements. A velocity mapping array has 128 elements.) Store the reassign value for a given data value in the element with the same index as the data value. (Reassign data for channel 3 is stored in channel array element 3, and so on.) This is an enhancement of the channel filter array used earlier.

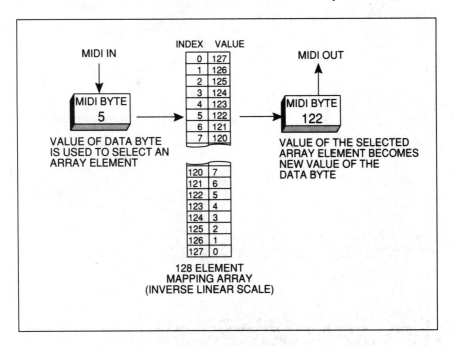

Mapping routines are quite simple, and they generally execute quickly enough to be transparent. They are so efficient that we frequently "hard wire" the mapping routine into the code so that the mapping mechanism is always active. When we don't want values to be reassigned, we simply initialize the array so that the value of each element is equal to its index number. This reassigns each value to itself, effectively turning the mapper off. The advantage of using a map is that all of the calculations needed to perform the reassignments to the values in the array are done ahead of time. When the program is processing MIDI in real-time, very little time is required to exchange the input value with the reassigned value. One disadvantage is the need to set aside memory for each array. As most MIDI data values are in the range of 0-127, the size of a single array is usually pretty small, but if you want to provide mapping for many ccontrollers, the amount of memory required could be prohibitive. (There are more than 100 controllers — many of them with 14-bit resolution). An alternative to using maps is to perform the reassign calculations in real-time.

Checking Values

MIDI Data Ranges			
Data Type	**Range**		**Notes**
	Hex	**Decimal**	
NOTE NUMBER	00-F7	0-127	60 = MIDDLE "C"
ATTACK VELOCITY	01-F7	1-127	0 = NOTE OFF
RELEASE VELOCITY	00-F7	0-127	
POLY KEY PRESSURE	00-F7	0-127	
14-BIT CONTROLLER IDs	00-3F	0-63	0-31 MSB, 32-63 LSB
7-BIT CONTROLLER IDs	40-5F	64-95	
+/- CONTROLLER IDs	60-65	96-101	
MIDI MODES (CONTROLLER ID)	79-7F	121-127	
CONTROLLER VALUE MSB	00-7F	0-127	ALL CONTROLLERS
CONTROLLER VALUE LSB	00-7F	0-127	CONTROLLERS 0-31 ONLY
PROGRAM ID NUMBER	00-F7	0-127	
CHANNEL PRESSURE	00-7F	0-127	
PITCH BEND MSB	00-7F	0-127	
PITCH BEND LSB	00-7F	0-127	
MTC QUARTER FRAME (MS NIBBLE)	0-7	0-7	MESSAGE NUMBER
MTC QUARTER FRAME (LS NIBBLE)	0-F	0-15	DATA
FRAME COUNT	00-1D	0-29	AFTER DE-NIBBLIZING
SECONDS COUNT	00-3B	0-59	AFTER DE-NIBBLIZING
MINUTES COUNT	00-3B	0-59	AFTER DE-NIBBLIZING
HOURS COUNT	00-17	0-23	AFTER DE-NIBBLIZING
SONG POSITION POINTER LSB	00-7F	0-127	
SONG POSITION POINTER MSB	00-7F	0-127	
SONG ID NUMBER	00-7F	0-127	
SYSEX IDs (MANUFACTURER)	00-7C	0-124	0=EXTENSION
SYSEX IDs (UNIVERSAL)	7D-7F	125-127	
MANUFACTURER ID EXTENSION #1	00	0	1-127 ARE UNASSIGNED
MANUFACTURER ID EXTENSION #2	00-F7	0-127	
NON-REAL TIME SYSEX SUB ID #1	00-7F	0-127	7-123 ARE UNASSIGNED
REAL TIME SYSEX SUB ID #1	01	1	0, 2-127 ARE UNASSIGNED
DEVICE CHANNEL	00-7F	0-127	127 = ALL DEVICES

Whenever you manipulate a MIDI data value, always check the resulting value to see if it is within the legal range of values for that data type. This is necessary whether you are manipulating values in an array or modifying a byte in real-time. In order to keep our examples brief and clear, we haven't included a lot of error checking routines. — That will be your job. The table on the previous page lists the legal values for different MIDI data types.

Channel Mapper

A channel mapping routine reassigns incoming messages on a given channel to another channel, then sends them to the MIDI Out port. The ProcessChannels routine we set up earlier can be modifed to include channel mapping by adding an ELSE clause to the procedure's single IF statement. Here's the new, channel-mapping version of the routine.

```
PROCEDURE  ProcessChannels;
  VAR
    channelNumber:  integer;
BEGIN
  channelNumber  :=  GetChannel(theMIDIByte);
  IF  Channel[channelNumber]  =  -1  THEN
    statusBuffer  :=  ignore
  ELSE
    theMIDIByte  :=  BitAND(theMIDIByte,  $F0)  +  Channel[channelNumber];
END;{ProcessChannels}
```

As before, the status byte's channel number is used to index a channel array. If the value of the indexed element is -1, the status buffer is cleared and nothing else happens. If the value is not -1, it is the reassignment value for that channel. This value is inserted into the lower four bits of the status byte, effectively reassigning the channel number. That's all there is to it! The reassignment is done with a simple calculation. First, the byte is ANDed with a status mask constant F0H. This returns a value with the status in the higher four bits, and the lower four bits are cleared. This is added to the value of the array element.

In order for the application to work properly when no reassignments are selected, the array must be initialized correctly at start-up. One way to set it up would be to have the progran start up with the elements "normalized" (channel[0] = 0, channel[1] = 1 ... channel[15] = 15. Then allow the user to change the values for any element in the array. Setting an element's value to -1 will filter that channel out of the data stream. Setting it to a value from 0-15 will reassign that channel to the new value. This routine shows how to intialize the array.

```
PROCEDURE  InitChannelMap;
  VAR
    count: integer;
BEGIN
    FOR count := 0 TO 15 DO
      channel[count] := count;
END;{InitChannelMap}
```

Note and Velocity Mapping

Mapping note numbers is basically the same as mapping channel numbers. We'll need an array with an element for every possible note number (128), a procedure to normalize the array, and a procedure containing a statement to re-assign a note number value to a value stored in the array. While we're at it we should also set up and initialize an array for velocity values. The note and velocity arrays are declared and initialized as follows.

```
VAR
  notes: ARRAY[0..127] OF integer;
  velocity: ARRAY[0..127] OF integer;

PROCEDURE  InitNoteMap;
  VAR
    count: integer;
BEGIN
    FOR count := 0 TO 127 DO
      note[count] := count;
END;{InitNoteMap}

PROCEDURE  InitVelocityMap;
{NOTE! Don't allow user to reassign the   }
{value of velocity zero! That value is     }
{used to signify "Note Off" If it is       }
{reassigned, notes may stay on.            }
{indefinitely                              }
  VAR
    count: integer;
BEGIN
    FOR count := 0 TO 127 DO
      velocity[count] := count;
END;{InitVelocityMap}
```

The note processing procedure is called from the NoteOff1..NoteOn16 block of the case-structure in ParseMIDI.

```
PROCEDURE ParseMIDI;
  .  .  .
  .  .  .
  NoteOff1..NoteOn16:
    IF NoteFlag THEN
      ProcessNotes;{Call Note processing routine}
    ELSE
    BEGIN
      statusBuffer := Ignore;
      dataCount := 0;
    END;  {Call Note processing routine}
  .  .  .
END;{ParseMIDI}
```

The processing procedure consists of a single case-structure with a case-statement for each byte in the message. The counter we created previously holds the order in the message of the current byte: 0=status byte, 1=first data byte, 2=second data byte, and so on. Each case-statement traps a particular byte in the message and can call a processing routine for that byte. The counter is updated at this point, so that the next data byte will be trapped by the appropriate case-statement. Note that, when the first and second bytes are processed, the counter is incremented by one but, when the third (last) byte is processed, the counter is set to 1. This insures that Running Status will be handled properly. If additional messages are sent under Running Status, the next byte will be the note number data byte. It will be trapped by the note number case-statement. If additional messages are sent under normal format, the next byte will be a status byte, and the counter will be cleared in UpdateStatus.

```
PROCEDURE  ProcessNotes;
BEGIN
  CASE dataCount OF

    0:{process  status  byte}
    BEGIN
      { status byte could be altered here }
      dataCount := dataCount +1;
    END;

    1:{process  note  number  byte}
    BEGIN
      theMIDIByte  :=  note[theMIDIByte];
      dataCount := dataCount +1;
    END;

    2:{process  velocity  value}
    BEGIN
      theMIDIByte  :=  velocity[theMIDIByte];
      dataCount := 1;
    END;
END;{ProcessNotes}
```

In our example, the status byte of the Note On/Off message isn't modified, but there is no reason why such a modification couldn't be added. For example, a filter could be added to allow you to filter out notes on a given channel. — Just check the channel number of the status byte against a "channel-selective note filter" hit-list. If they match, clear the statusBuffer. That's all there is to it. This same idea can be used with any of the other Channel Voice messages.

Program Number Mapping

You are not limited to modifying channel, note, and velocity values. The same principals can be applied to MIDI data from any other Channel message. Here's how to set an array and processing procedure to reassign MIDI program numbers.

```
VAR
  program: ARRAY[0..127] OF integer;

PROCEDURE  InitProgramMap;
  VAR
    count: integer;
BEGIN
  FOR count := 0 TO 127 DO
    program[count] := count;
END;{InitProgramMap}
```

The Program Change processing procedure is called from the "ProgramChange1 .. ProgramChange16" block of the case structure in ParseMIDI.

```
Procedure  ParseMIDI;
. . .
. . .
  ProgramChange1..ProgramChange16  :
    IF PChangeFlag THEN
      ProcessPChange;{Call Program processing routine}
    ELSE
    BEGIN
      statusBuffer := Ignore;
      dataCount := 0;
    END;  {Call Program processing routine}
. . .
. . .
END;  {ParseMIDI}
```

The Program Change processing procedure is similar to the one used to process notes. It is made up of a single case-structure with a block for each byte in the message.

```
PROCEDURE  ProcessPChange;
BEGIN
  CASE dataCount OF

    0:{process  status  byte}
    BEGIN
      { status  byte  could  be  altered  here }
      dataCount  :=  dataCount  +1;
    END;

    1:{process  note  number  byte}
    BEGIN
      theMIDIByte  :=  program[theMIDIByte];
      dataCount  :=  dataCount  +1;
    END;
END;{ProcessPChange}
```

Control Mapping

Mapping the data in Control Change messages is a bit trickier than mapping the other types of Channel Message data. Here are some of the things to keep in mind.

- The range of "legal" controller ID values is 0-120. The practical range is 0-31 (14-bit MSBs) and 64-95 (7-bit controllers).

- Values above 120 are Channel Mode messages. They should not be processed by Control Change routines.

- It isn't practical to provide a separate control value array for each possible controller ID. This would require that a great deal of RAM be allocated for controller arrays. (You wouldn't expect all 95 controllers to be used while the program is running anyway.) A more practical choice might be to provide a single-channel value array that is used by all controllers, or to use a manageable set of arrays.

- If you use multiple arrays, you'll have to provide a mechanism for linking selected controller IDs to the appropriate arrays.

Here is the code required to set up controller ID mapping and a single-controller value map.

```
VAR
  program: ARRAY[0..127] OF integer;

PROCEDURE  InitControlIDMap;
  {Do not let the user alter the values of  }
  {elements 121-127! These are the IDs of   }
  {Channel Mode messages, They should never }
  {be reassigned by a controller routine    }

  VAR
    count: integer;
BEGIN
    FOR count := 0 TO 127 DO
      controlID[count] := count;
END;{InitControlIDMap}


PROCEDURE  InitControlValueMap;
  VAR
    count: integer;
BEGIN
    FOR count := 0 TO 127 DO
      controlValue[count] := count;
END;{InitControlValueMap}


PROCEDURE ParseMIDI;
.  .  .
.  .  .
  ControlChange1..ControlChange16  :
    IF PChangeFlag THEN
      ProcessCChange;{Call Control processing routine}
    ELSE
    BEGIN
      statusBuffer := Ignore;
      dataCount := 0;
    END; {Call Control processing routine}
.  .  .
.  .  .
END;{ParseMIDI}
```

```
PROCEDURE  ProcessCChange;
BEGIN
  CASE dataCount OF

    0:{process  status  byte}
    BEGIN
      { status byte could be altered here }
      dataCount := dataCount +1;
    END;

    1:{process  controller  ID  byte}
    BEGIN
      theMIDIByte := controlID[theMIDIByte];
      dataCount := dataCount +1;
    END;

    2:{process  controller  value}
    BEGIN
      theMIDIByte := controlValue[theMIDIByte];
      dataCount := 0;
    END;
END;{ProcessCChange}
```

Generic Processing Routines

Routines to call processing for each of the other Channel Voice and System Common (except System Exclusive) messages are exactly the same, except that some of them require only two case-statements. Here are sample array declarations and a procedure shell for any 3-byte message: Note Off, Note On, Poly Key Pressure, Control Change, Pitch Wheel Change, Song Position Pointer.

```
VAR
  data1: ARRAY[0..127] OF integer;
  data2: ARRAY[0..127] OF integer;

PROCEDURE  InitData1Map;
  VAR
    count: integer;
BEGIN
    FOR count := 0 TO 127 DO
      data1[count] := count;
END;{InitData1Map}


PROCEDURE  InitData2Map;
  VAR
    count: integer;
BEGIN
    FOR count := 0 TO 127 DO
      data2[count] := count;
END;{InitData2Map}



PROCEDURE  Process3ByteMessages;
  BEGIN
    CASE dataCount OF

      0:{process status byte}
      BEGIN
        { status byte could be altered here }
        dataCount := dataCount +1;
      END;

      1:{process byte 1}
      BEGIN
        theMIDIByte := data1[theMIDIByte];
        dataCount := dataCount +1;
      END;

      2:{process byte 2}
      BEGIN
        theMIDIByte := data2[theMIDIByte];
        dataCount := 1;
      END;
    END;{Process3ByteMessages}
```

Following are the array declarations and procedure shell for any 2-byte message: Program Change, Channel Pressure, MTC Quarter Frame, Song Select.

```
VAR
  data1: ARRAY[0..127] OF integer;

PROCEDURE  InitData1Map;
  VAR
    count: integer;
BEGIN
    FOR count := 0 TO 127 DO
      data1[count] := count;
END;{InitData1Map}



PROCEDURE  Process2ByteMessages;
  BEGIN
    CASE dataCount OF

      0:{process status byte}
      BEGIN
        { status byte could be altered here }
        dataCount := dataCount +1;
      END;

      1:{process byte 1}
      BEGIN
        theMIDIByte := data1[theMIDIByte];
        dataCount := 1;
      END;
  END;{Process2ByteMessages}
```

Here is the complete ParseMIDI procedure showing where the calls for each
Channel Message Type would be installed.

```
PROCEDURE ParseMIDI;
BEGIN
{Parse status/data and process System Messages}
   IF theMIDIByte >= NoteOff1 THEN{parse status bytes from data bytes}
   BEGIN
     UpdateStatus;                        {update buffer if necessary}
     IF (theMIDIByte < SysEx) AND (ChannelFlag) THEN
       ProcessChannels;    {Call Channel processing routine}
   END;

{Parse Channel Message bytes and process recognized messages}
   CASE statusBuffer OF                 {process byte based on status}
     Ignore:
       ; {do nothing with unrecognized status or data bytes}
   {call processing routines for recognized status types}

     NoteOff1..NoteOn16:
       IF NoteFlag THEN
   {Call Note processing routine}
       ELSE
       BEGIN
         statusBuffer := Ignore;
         dataCount := 0;
       END; {Call Note processing routine}

     PolyPress1..PolyPress16:
       IF PPressFlag THEN
   {Call Poly Pressure processing routine}
       ELSE
       BEGIN
         statusBuffer := Ignore;
         dataCount := 0;
       END;

     ControlChange1..ControlChange16:
       IF CChangeFlag THEN
   {Call Control Change processing routine}
       ELSE
       BEGIN
         statusBuffer := Ignore;
         dataCount := 0;
       END;
```

```
  ProgramChange1..ProgramChange16:
    IF PChangeFlag THEN
{Call P Change processing routine}
    ELSE
    BEGIN
     statusBuffer := Ignore;
     dataCount := 0;
    END;

  ChanPress1..ChanPress16:
    IF CPressFlag THEN
{Call Channel Pressure processing routine}
    ELSE
    BEGIN
     statusBuffer := Ignore;
     dataCount := 0;
    END;

  PitchWheel1..PitchWheel16:
    IF PWheelFlag THEN
{Call P Wheel processing routine}
    ELSE
    BEGIN
     statusBuffer := Ignore;
     dataCount := 0;
    END;

  OTHERWISE
    ; {bytes belong to unrecognized status, do nothing}
  END;{CASE statusBuffer}
END; {ParseMIDI}
```

Creating Maps

At this point, our program has a lot of potential and flexibility. Here's a summary of what it can already do:

- Filter out all messages on any channel(s)

- Reassign message on any channel to any other channel

- Filter out any type of Channel Message

- Filter out any type of Channel Message on any channel

- Reassign any note number to any other note number

- Reassign any velocity value to any other velocity value

- Reassign messages from any controller ID to any other controller ID

- Reassign any controller value to any other controller value

The last four points have the most potential. Think a bit about what it means to be able to reassign any note number, velocity value, controller ID, or controller value. Want to transpose a MIDI sound source up an octave? Simple — just add 12 to the initialized note array values. Want control modulation parameters with breath pressure? Reassign the breath pressure ID to the modulation ID. Want to rescale an instrument's repsonse to breath pressure? Modify the array values for a non-linear response.

You can see that there are many possibilities. All you have to do is rearrange the values of the elements in the mapping arrays. The processing routines described will take care of the rest. Here are some examples of mapping arrays for various effects.

Linear Map

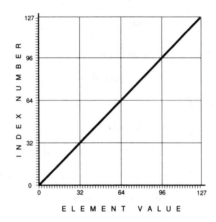

In our routines, the mapping algorithm is used constantly, whether or not you want to reassign a value. A linear map is used when no reassignment effects are desired. The map is initialized by setting the value of each element to the value of its index number.

Inverse Linear Map

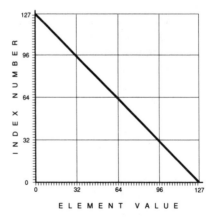

An inverse linear map is used to produce the opposite of the effect normally associated with a range of values. It can be used, for example, to make notes get softer as attack velocity increases, or to reverse the note-order on a keyboard, making pitches higher as you play down a scale.

Replace with Constant

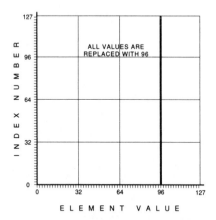

This map reassigns all values to a single constant. This could be used to remove the dynamics from Note On messages, making them uniformly loud, regardless of the velocity used. Another use might be to reassign all pitches to a single pitch. This would allow you to control a mono-pitched percussion voice with a multi-pitched melody.

Log Map

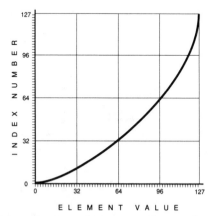

This map reassigns values on a log curve. This can be used to customize the response to any controller, so the sensitivity to changes increases towards the top-end of the controller's range. It can also be used to rescale the velocity response of an instrument, making it more responsive to higher velocities and less responsive to lower ones.

Anti-Log Map

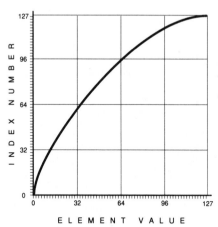

This map reassigns values in the opposite manner of the log map, thereby producing the opposite effect. Sensitivity is greater at the bottom of the range than at the top.

Negative Offset

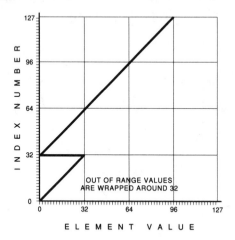

This map is used to reassign all values by a constant, negative amount. Elements with index numbers below the offset value would be shifted out of the legal MIDI data range (below zero), so they must be "wrapped around" some value. (In the graph shown, all incoming values are reduced by 32; out-of-range values are wrapped around zero.) A negative offset could be used to transpose all notes down be a fixed interval, or to lower the overall loudness of a series of notes while preserving their relative dynamics.

Positive Offset

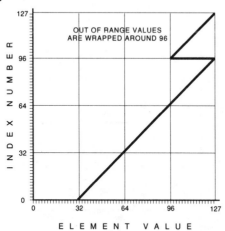

This map reassigns values in the opposite manner of the negative offset map. (In the graph shown, all incoming values are increased by 32; out-of-range values are wrapped around 96.) This will produce effects that are the opposite of a negative offset map.

Shelfing Map

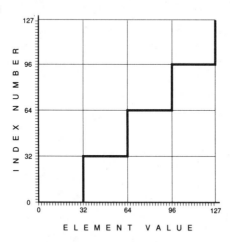

This map reassigns incoming values to a series of discrete steps. This divides the overall range of values into a small set of two or more values. (In the graph shown, the overall range of incoming values is divided into four values.) If the map shown were applied to modulation values, moving the mod wheel from minimum to maximum would produce only four distinct modulation amounts: none, slight, moderate, and maximum.

Zoning Map

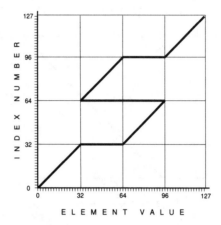

This map is divided into several zones. Each of these zones is a separate linear map with a positive or negative offset. When used to reassign note numbers, this map allows you to divide a MIDI keyboard into several pitch areas. Each area can be tranposed up or down, independently.

Processing SysEx Message Types

Unlike other MIDI messages, System Exclusive (SysEx) message types are not completely identified by the value of the status byte. Depending on the type of SysEx message, they are identified by the value of one or more data bytes. The value of the byte following the SysEx status byte identifies the message as one of five general SysEx message types: 3-byte manufacturer ID, 1-byte manufacturer ID, Universal Non-Commercial, Universal Non-Real-Time or Unversal Real-Time. Since the formats of these messages are so different from Channel or other System Common messages, the parsing techniques are different as well. The general steps for parsing SysEx messages from within our example MIDI parsing structure are as follows.

```
Main parsing routine:
        Get a byte from the MIDI In port
        If the byte is a status byte update the status buffer

Update status buffer:
        If byte = 80-EFH, byte is Channel message status
                set status buffer to value of the byte
                clear counter

        If byte = F0H, byte is System Exclusive
                clear status buffer
                clear counter
                If SysEx messages are recognized
                        process SysEx message

        If byte = F1- F7H, byte is System Common
                clear status buffer
                clear counter

        If byte = F8H-FFH, byte is System Real-Time
                don't change status buffer (interrupt Running Status)
                process System Real-Time if recognized

Process SysEx message:
        Get a byte from the MIDI In port
        Check if byte is data or status
        If the byte is a status
                stop processing SysEx
                Update the status buffer
        If byte is data
                process SysEx message type
```

Note that, once a SysEx status byte has been recognized, we can't know which type of SysEx message will follow until we get the next byte in the message. Although we'd like to assume that the next byte will be a data byte for the SysEx message, it could, in fact, be a status byte. (Reception of a status byte at this point, though unlikely, is a possibility. For example, a prioritized System Real-Time status byte could arrive.) When the next byte is received, it must be tested to see if it's a data or a status byte. What happens at that point depends on the value of the byte. There are three possibilities.

- If it's a data byte, process it as part of the SysEx message. Its value will determine the type of message.

- If it's a Channel or System Common status byte, update the status buffer and return to the calling routine without processing the SysEx message.

- If it's a System Real-Time status byte, process the message immediately (if recognized), get another byte, and check to see if it is the expected data byte or an unexpected status byte.

The test should always be made, because an unidentified status byte would throw off the logic of both the System Exclusive and the main MIDI parsing routines. At the very least, the SysEx message would not be interpreted properly, and the message signified by the untested status byte would be lost. This test should be performed on every single byte of any SysEx message, as an unexpected status byte could show up at any time. There is also a special case to consider. The last byte of all SysEx messages must be an EOX (F7H) status byte. To accomodate this, the data test should not simply abort processing of SysEx messages if a status byte arrives. Instead, it should set a flag to tell the calling routine that a status byte was detected, and let the calling routine decide what to do. (This will make it easier to handle SysEx messages with variable lengths since the calling routine can use the test to check for the terminating EOX, as well as any unexpected status bytes.) The following outline details the design of general purpose test that could be used by all SysEx processing routines.

```
Check if byte is data or status:
        If byte = 0-7FH, byte is data
                set flag to data = true

        If byte = 80H-F7H, byte is Channel or System Common status
                update the status buffer
                set flag to data = false

        If byte = F8H-FFH, byte is System Real-Time
                process System Real-Time (if recognized)
                get a byte from the MIDI In port
                check if byte is data or status
```

Assuming that the byte turns out to be the expected data byte, we can now determine the type of SysEx message we're receiving: 3-byte Manufacturer ID, 1-byte Manufacturer ID, Non-Real-Time SysEx, or Real-Time SysEx.

If the byte's value is 0, a 3-byte Manufacturer ID message is being received and a procedure to process this type of message is called. If the byte's value is in the range of 1-7CH, a 1-byte Manufacturer ID message is coming in. The value of the byte will determine which specific routine to call. (There will be a separate routine for each recognized manufacturer ID.) If the value of the byte is 7EH, a routine for processsing Non-Real-Time SysEx messages is called. If the byte's value is 7FH a routine for processing Real-Time SysEx messages is called.

```
Process SysEx message type:
        If the byte = 0, message is for 3-byte manufacturer ID
                process 3-byte manufacturer ID message

        If byte = 1-7CH, message is 1-byte manufacturer ID
                process recognized 1-byte manufacturer ID message

        If byte = 7EH, message is Non-Real-Time SysEx
                process Non-Real-Time SysEx message

        If byte = 7F, message is Real-Time SysEx
                process Real-Time SysEx message
```

Procedures for a SysEx Processing Shell

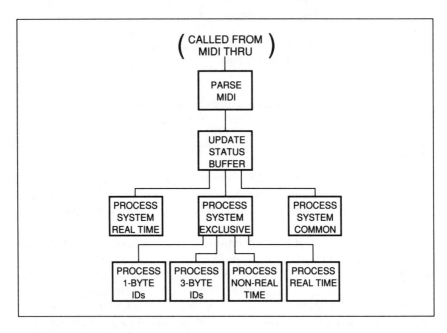

Let's expand our sample program to allow it to recognize System Exclusive data, using the outlines for SysEx routines as a guide. The original version of UpdateStatus included a trap for the SysEx status bytes. In that version of the procedure, whenever a SysEx status byte was received the status buffer was cleared and SysEx messages were simply ignored. Here's how the original version looked.

```
PROCEDURE UpdateStatus;
BEGIN
  CASE theMIDIByte OF
  . . .
  . . .

    SysEX:
    BEGIN
      statusBuffer := Ignore;    {ignore these messages for now}
      dataCount := 0;            {new status, reset value of dataCount}
    END;
  . . .
  . . .
  END; {CASE theMIDIByte}
END; {UpdateStatusBuffer}
```

We'll modify the program to allow use of a flag variable that can turn on and off the reception of System Exclusive messages. The SysEx case-statement in UpdateStatus is expanded by adding a test for the flag. When the flag is false, System Exclusive messages will be ignored. When it is true, they will be processed. Note that we choose to process SysEx mesages from here, in UpdateStatus, instead of processing them after returning to ParseMIDI. After the message is processed by the ProcessSysEx procedure, the status buffer and counter are cleared, and control returns to ParseMIDI.

```
VAR
  SysExFlag: Boolean;               {used to turn SysEx processing on/off}
PROCEDURE UpdateStatus;
BEGIN
CASE theMIDIByte
    . . .
    . . .
    SysEx:
    BEGIN
      IF SysExFlag THEN             {ignore SysEx if flag = false}
        ProcessSysEx;              {call SysEx processing routine}
      statusBuffer := Ignore;
      dataCount := 0;
      END;
    . . .
    . . .
END; {CASE theMIDIByte}
END; {UpdateStatusBuffer}
```

As we pointed out earlier, all of the SysEx processing routines will provide a check of every incoming byte to see if it is data or status. If it's a data byte, the processing can continue. If it's a status byte other than an expected EOX status byte signifying the last byte of the message, the processing should stop and the incomplete SysEx message should be ignored. Instead of inserting lines of test code into every SysEx procedure, we can create a general purpose function to perform the test. Then, any byte within any routine can be tested, with a single function call.

The following function, SysExData, tests the value of the global variable, theMIDIByte. The function evaluates "true" if theMIDIByte is a data byte, and "false" if it is a System Common or Channel message status byte. A case-structure is used to perform the test. If theMIDIByte is data (0-7FH), the value of the function is set to true and control returns to the calling routine. If theMIDIbyte is a Channel or System Common status byte, UpdateStatus is called to reset the status buffer and clear the counter. The value of the function is then set to false, and control returns to the calling routine. If theMIDIByte is a System Real-Time byte, it is processed immediately (if it is recognized by the application). Since Real-Time messages can legally interrupt a SysEx message, at this point the SysEx processing should continue as if the Real-Time byte never arrived. The next byte is received and the function calls itself to perform the data check.

```
FUNCTION SysExData: Boolean;
BEGIN
  CASE theMIDIByte OF
    $0..$7F:                      {byte was data, tell calling}
      SysExData := True;          {routine it's OK to process}

    NoteOff1..EOX:                {byte was status byte,}
    BEGIN
      UpdateStatus;               {update status buffer}
      SysExData := False;         {warn the calling routine}
    END;

    TimingClock..SystemReset:     {byte was Real-Time,}
    BEGIN
      ; {process Real-Time messages if recognized}
      ReadMIDI(theMIDIByte);      {get the next byte}
      SysExData := SysExData;     {check to see if it's data}
    END;
  END;
END; {SysExData}
```

Now that we have a function to test for SysEx data, we can build the first level routine for processing SysEx messages. This procedure is called from UpdateStatus whenever a SysEx status byte is received and the SysExFlag is set to recognize SysEx messages. ProcessSysEx gets the next byte from the MIDI In buffer and uses the SysExData function to check the byte. If SysEx data is false, then the byte was a status byte, and the procedure is exited. Control returns to UpdateStatus. If SysEx data is true, the byte was byte 2 of the SysEx message. The value of this byte specifies the type of SysEx message. A case-structure uses the value of the byte to select the processing routine for the SysEx type. If the value of the byte is 0, the routine for processing 3-byte Manufacturer ID messages is called. If the value is 7EH, the routine for processing Non-Real-Time SysEx messages is called. If the value is 7FH, the the routine for processing Real-Time SysEx messages is called. If the value is 1-7CH, it is a 1-byte Manufacturer ID message. To process these messages, include a separate case-statement for each Manufactuer ID recognized. (See ?) We've included case-statements for Lexicon, Kurzweil, Roland, and Korg System Exclusive messages to show how routines for specific manufacturers would be called.

```
PROCEDURE ProcessSysEx;
BEGIN
  ReadMIDI(theMIDIByte);          {get SysEx byte 2 }
  IF SysExData = False THEN
    Exit(ProcessSysEx);           {stop if byte isn't data}

  CASE theMIDIByte OF             {parse SysEx byte 2}
    0:
      Process3ByteID;
    $06:
      ; {process Lexicon SysEx}
    $07:
      ; {process Kurzweil SysEx}
    $41:
      ; {process Roland SysEx}
    $42:
      ; {process Korg SysEx}
    $7E:
      ProcessNonRealSysEx;
    $7F:
      ProcessRealSysEx;
    OTHERWISE
      ; {SysEx type is not recognized, do nothing}
  END;
END;
```

Parsing SysEx Types

When the second byte of a SysEx message is 0, 7EH, or 7FH, it will be necessary to receive two or three additional bytes to determine the specific message. If the byte is 0, then the message is a 3-byte Manufacturer ID message. The next two bytes (ID #1 and ID #2) will identify the specific manufacturer. The following outline shows how to parse the ID bytes to select the proper manufacturer.

```
Process 3-byte ID message:
Get ID #1:
        Check if byte is data or status.
        If the byte is a status
                stop processing SysEx
        If byte is data ,byte is ID #1
        If byte = 0, get ID #2

Get ID #2:
        Check if byte is data or status.
        If the byte is a status
                stop processing SysEx
        If byte is data ,byte is ID #2
                process recognized 3-byte Manufactuer ID message
```

When the second byte of the SysEx message equals 7EH, a Non-Real-Time SysEx message is being processed. Three additional bytes must be received. The first of these is the device ID. The value of this byte is used to route it to a specific device. If the device ID matches the application's unit number, or if the device ID is 127, the message should be recognized. If the device ID is not 127, or does not match the applcation's unit number, the message should be ignored. If the device ID is recognized, then the next two bytes (ID#1 and ID #2) will identify the specific Non-Real-Time message to be processed. The following outline shows how to parse the device ID and sub-ID#1 bytes to select a routine to process the appropriate message.

Process Non-Real-Time SysEx:
Get Device ID:

Check if byte is data or status.

If the byte is a status
stop processing SysEx

If byte is data ,byte is device ID
If byte = unit number OR 127
get sub-ID #1
If byte   unit number OR 127
stop processing SysEx

Get sub-ID #1:
Check if byte is data or status.
If the byte is a status
stop processing SysEx
If byte is data ,byte is ID #1
If byte = 1,process Sample Dump Header
If byte = 2, process Sample Dump Data
If byte = 3, process Sample Dump Request
If byte = 4, process MTC Setup
If byte = 5, process Sample Dump Extension
If byte = 6, process Device Inquiry
If byte = 7CH, process Wait
If byte = 7DH, process Cancel
If byte = 7EH, process ACK
If byte = 7FH, process NAK

Note that there are currently ten types of Non-Real-Time SysEx messages specified by the value of sub-ID #1. With the exception of the seven messages defined in the Sample Dump Standard (Dump Header, Dump Data, Dump Request, Wait, Cancel, ACK, and NAK), all Non-Real-Time messages are specified by two sub-IDs. Sub-ID #1 specifies the type of Non-Real-Time SysEx message and sub-ID #2 specifies a particular message of that type. There are currently three Non-Real-Time SysEx message types: MIDI Time Code Set-Up (sub-ID #2=2), Sample Dump Extension (sub-ID #2=3), and Device Inquiry (sub-ID #2=4). The following outlines detail how to parse the sub-ID # 2 byte for each of the three types.

Process MTC Set-Up :
    Get sub-ID #2:
    Check if byte is data or status.
    If the byte is a status
        stop processing SysEx
    If byte is data , byte is sub-ID #2
        If byte = 0, process Special message
        If byte = 1 or 2, process Punch In/Out
        If byte = 3 or 4, process Delete Punch In/Out
        If byte = 5 or 6, process Event Start/Stop
        If byte = 7 or 8, process Event Start/Stop + info
        If byte = 9 or 0AH, process Delete Event Start/Stop
        If byte = 0BH, process Cue Points
        If byte = 0CH, process Cue Points + info
        If byte = 0DH, process Delete Cue Points
        If byte = 0EH, process Event Name in info

Process Sample Dump Extension :
Get sub-ID #2:
    Check if byte is data or status.
    If the byte is a status
        stop processing SysEx
    If byte is data ,byte is sub-ID #2
        If byte = 1, process Multiple Loop Points message
        If byte = 2, process Loop Points Request message

Process Device Inquiry :
Get sub-ID #2:
    Check if byte is data or status.
    If the byte is a status
        stop processing SysEx
    If byte is data ,byte is sub-ID #2
        If byte = 1, process Device ID Request message
        If byte = 2, process Device ID Replay message

When the second byte of the SysEx message equals 7FH, a Real-Time SysEx message is being processed. The general format of these messages is the same as for two sub-ID Non-Real-Time messages. Three additional bytes must be received. The first byte is the device ID. If the device ID matches the application's unit number, or if the device ID is 127, the message should be recognized. If the device ID is not 127, or does not match the application's unit number, the message should be ignored. If the device ID is recognized, then the next two bytes (sub-ID #1 and sub-ID #2) will identify the specific Real-Time message to be processed. The following outline shows how to parse the device ID and sub-ID # 1 bytes to select a routine to process the appropriate message.

Process Real-Time SysEx:
Get Device ID:
        Check if byte is data or status.
        If the byte is a status
                stop processing SysEx

        If byte is data , byte is device ID
                If byte = unit number OR 127
                        get sub-ID #1
                If byte   unit number OR 127
                        stop processing SysEx

Get sub-ID #1:
        Check if byte is data or status.
        If the byte is a status
                stop processing SysEx
        If byte is data , byte is sub-ID #1
                If byte = 1, process MTC

MTC (MIDI Time Code) is the only type of Real-Time SysEx message currently defined (ID #1=1). The following outline shows how to parse the sub-ID #2 byte for MTC messages.

Process MTC :
Get sub-ID #2:
        Check if byte is data or status.
        If the byte is a status
                stop processing SysEx
        If byte is data ,byte is sub-ID #2
                If byte = 1, process Full Message
                If byte = 2, process User Bits message

Procedures for Parsing SysEx Message Types

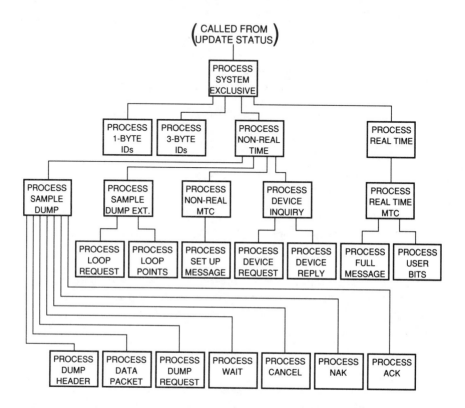

Using the previous outlines as a guide, we can develop code for parsing SysEx messages by type. The previously described ProcessSysEx procedure calls the appropriate SysEx parsing routine, according to the value of the second byte of a SysEx message. If the value of this byte is in the range of 1-7CH, the message is a 1-byte Manufacturer ID message. A manufactuer-specific SysEx routine is called directly from ProcessSysEx. (We'll look at a manufacuturer-specific roiutine later on in *Processing SysEx Messages*.) If the value of the second byte of the SysEx message is outside of the range of 1-7CH, one of three intermediate procedures is called. These procedures are used to parse the different messages for each of the remaining three types of SysEx messages: 3-byte Manufacturer ID, Non-Real-Time SysEx, and Real-Time SysEx. (Non-Commerical SysEx messages are ignored. This type of message will never be transmitted by a commercial device.) The code for ProcessSysEx is repeated here, and the code relating to the three intermediate procedures follows.

```
PROCEDURE ProcessSysEx;
BEGIN
  ReadMIDI(theMIDIByte);          {get SysEx byte 2 }
  IF SysExData = False THEN
    Exit(ProcessSysEx);           {stop if byte isn't data}

  CASE theMIDIByte OF             {parse SysEx byte 2}
    0:
      Process3ByteID;
    $06:
      ; {process Lexicon SysEx}
    $07:
      ; {process Kurzweil SysEx}
    $41:
      ; {process Roland SysEx}
    $42:
      ; {process Korg SysEx}
    $7E:
      ProcessNonRealSysEx;
    $7F:
      ProcessRealSysEx;
    OTHERWISE
      ; {SysEx type is not recognized, do nothing}
  END;
END;
```

3-Byte Manufacturer ID SysEx Messages

When Process3ByteID is called, it gets the next byte from the MIDI In buffer and uses the SysExData function to check its value. If the function evaluates false, a status byte has arrived. The SysEx message is not processed further, and control returns to the calling routine (UpdateStatus). If SysExData evaluates true, then the value of theMIDIByte is ID#1 of a 3-byte Manufacturer ID message. A case-structure with a statement for each defined ID #1 value is used to parse this byte. As of this writing, the only defined value for ID #1 is zero. Additional case-statements can be added as new ID #1 values are defined. After ID #1 is received and parsed, the next byte in the message should be ID #2. Once again, a byte is retrieved and checked with SysExData. If the byte is a data byte, its value is a manufacturer-specific ID. Another case-structure is used to parse ID #2. It contains a case-statement for each recognized manufacturer ID. The manufacturer-specific SysEx routines are called directly from the appropriate case-statement.

```
PROCEDURE Process3ByteID;
BEGIN
  ReadMIDI(theMIDIByte);        {get ID byte 1}
  IF SysExData = False THEN
    Exit(Process3ByteID);{stop if byte isn't data}

  CASE theMIDIByte OF           {parse ID byte 1}
    0:
    BEGIN
      ReadMIDI(theMIDIByte);    {get ID byte 2}
      IF SysExData = False THEN
        Exit(Process3ByteID);   {stop if byte isn't data}

      CASE theMIDIByte OF       {parse ID byte 2}

        $07:
          ; {process Digital Music Corp SysEx}
        $0B:
          ; {process IVL Technologies SysEx}
        $10:
          ; {process DOD SysEx}
        OTHERWISE
          ; {unrecognized Manufacturer ID 2, do nothing}
      END; {Case for ID #2}
    END; {ID 1 = 0 block}
    OTHERWISE
      ;{unrecognized ID 1, do nothing}
  END; {Case for ID 1}
END;{Process3ByteID}
```

Non-Real-Time SysEx Messages

The third byte of all Non-Real-Time SysEx messages is the device ID. This value is used to specify which receivers should recognize the message. If the value is 7FH, the message is meant for all receivers. If not, the message should only be recognized by receivers with a matching unit number. (The unit number can be the receiver's basic channel or any number from 0-126.) We'll declare two global variables: one to hold the application's unit number, the other to hold the device ID number of an incoming message.

```
VAR
  unitNumber: integer;    {device ID of this program}
  devChan: integer; {device ID in Universal SysEx messages}
```

When ProcessNonRealSysEx is called, it gets the next byte from the MIDI In buffer and checks its value with SysExData. If this byte is a status byte, the SysEx message is not processed any further, and control returns to UpdateStatus. If the byte is a data byte, its value is the device ID value of the message. This value is tested. If the device ID doesn't match the unit number and the device ID isn't 127 the message isn't processed any further and control returns to UpdateStatus. If the device ID is 127, or the device ID matches the unit number, the next byte of the message is received and tested with SysExData. If this byte is a data byte, its value is sub-ID #1 of the message. A case-structure is used to parse sub-ID #1.

There are currently ten defined sub-ID #1 values for Non-Real-Time messages. A case-statement for each one recognized by the application is included in the case-structure. If sub-ID #1 is for one of the seven Sample Dump Standard messages, the routine for processing the message is called directly from the corresponding case-statement. If sub-ID #1 value is 2, 3, or 4 (or any future defined sub-ID #1 value), an intermediate routine is called to parse the sub-ID #2 byte for the specific Non-Real-Time message type (MTC Set-Up, Sample Dump Extension, Device Inquiry).

```
PROCEDURE ProcessNonRealSysEx;
BEGIN
  ReadMIDI(theMIDIByte);          {get device ID byte}
  IF SysExData = False THEN
    Exit(ProcessNonRealSysEx);  {stop if byte isn't data}

  IF (theMIDIByte <> 127) AND (theMIDIByte <> unitNumber) THEN
    Exit(ProcessNonRealSysEx);  {stop if device ID s don't match}

  ReadMIDI(theMIDIByte);          {get sub-ID #1}
  IF SysExData = False THEN
    Exit(ProcessNonRealSysEx);  {stop if byte isn't data}

  CASE theMIDIByte OF             {parse sub-ID #1}
    1:
      GetSDHeader;{process SD Header}
    2:
      ;{process SD Data Packet}
    3:
      ;{process SD Request}
    4:
      ProcessMTCSetUp;{process MIDI TIME CODE messages}
    5:
      ProcessSDExt;{process SAMPLE DUMP EXTENSION messages}
    6:
      ProcessDevInquiry;{process DEVICE INQUIRY messages}
    $7C:
      ;{process Wait}
    $7D:
      ;{process Cancel}
    $7E:
      ;{process ACK}
    $7F:
      ;{process NAK}


    OTHERWISE
      ;{unrecognized sub-ID #1, do nothing}
  END; {Case for Non-Real-Time sub-ID #1}
END; {ProcessNonRealSysEx}
```

MTC Set-Up Messages

When this procedure is called, the next byte in the SysEx message (sub-ID #2) will indicate which of the fifteen defined MIDI Set-Up messages to process. The byte is checked with SysExData. If it is a data byte, a case-structure is used to parse the byte. The routine to process the specified MTC Set-Up message is called from the corresponding case-statement.

```
PROCEDURE ProcessMTCSetUp;
BEGIN
  ReadMIDI(theMIDIByte);           {get sub-ID #2}
  IF SysExData = False THEN
    Exit(ProcessMTCSetUp);         {stop if byte isn't data}

  CASE theMIDIByte OF              {parse sub-ID #2}
    0:
     ;{Special}
    1, 2:
     GetPunchInTime(theMIDIByte);{Punch In/Out}
    3, 4:
     ; {Delete Punch In/Out}
    5, 6:
     ; {Event Start/Stop}
    7, 8:
     ; {Event Start/Stop + Info}
    9, $A:
     ; {Delete Event Start/Stop}
    $B:
     ; {Cue Points}
    $C:
     ;{Cue Points + Info}
    $D:
     ;{Delete Cue Points}
    $E:
     ;{Event Name in Info}
    OTHERWISE
     ; {unrecognized MTC sub-ID #2, do nothing}
  END; {Case for sub-ID #2}
END;{ProcessMTCSetUp}
```

Sample Dump Extension Messages

When this procedure is called, the next byte in the SysEx message (sub-ID #2) will indicate which of the two defined Sample Dump Extension messages to process. The byte is checked with SysExData. If it is a data byte, a case-structure is used to parse the byte. The routine to process the specified Sample Dump Extension message is called from the corresponding case-statement.

```
PROCEDURE ProcessSDExt;
BEGIN
  ReadMIDI(theMIDIByte);          {get sub-ID #2}
  IF SysExData = False THEN
    Exit(ProcessSDExt);           {stop if byte isn't data}

  CASE theMIDIByte OF             {parse sub-ID #2}
    1:
      ; {Multiple Loop Points}
    2:
      ; {Loop Points Request}

    OTHERWISE
      ; {unrecognized SD Extension sub-ID #2, do nothing}
  END; {Case for sub-ID #2}
END;{ProcessSDExt}
```

Device Inquiry Messages

When this procedure is called, the next byte in the SysEx message (sub-ID #2) will indicate which of the two defined Device Inquiry messages to process. The byte is checked with SysExData. If it is a data byte, a case-structure is used to parse the byte. The routine to process the specified Device Inquiry message is called from the corresponding case-statement.

```
PROCEDURE ProcessDevInquiry;
BEGIN
  ReadMIDI(theMIDIByte);          {get sub-ID #2}
  IF SysExData = False THEN
    Exit(ProcessDevInquiry);      {stop if byte isn't data}

  CASE theMIDIByte OF             {parse sub-ID #2}
    1:
      ; {Device ID Request}
    2:
      ; {Device ID Reply}
    OTHERWISE
      ; {unrecognized Device Inquiry sub-ID #2, do nothing}
  END; {Case for sub-ID #2}
END;{ProcessDevInquiry}
```

Real-TIme SysEx Messages

The header of Real-Time SysEx messages is the same as for two- sub-ID Non-Real-Time messages. The procedure for parsing theses messages by type is built on the same shell as the one used for Non-Real-Time messages. The third byte of all Real-Time SysEx messages is the device ID . We'll use the two previously declared global variables to hold the unit number, and the device ID number of an incoming message. When ProcessRealSysEx is called it gets the next byte from the MIDI In buffer and checks its value with SysExData. If this byte is a status byte, the SysEx message is not processed any further and control returns to UpdateStatus. If the byte is a data byte, its value is the device ID value of the message. This value is tested. If the device ID doesn't match the unit number, and the device ID isn't 127, the message isn't processed any further and control returns to UpdateStatus. If the device ID is 127, or the device ID matches the unit number, the next byte of the message is received and tested with SysExData. If this byte is a data byte, its value is sub-ID #1 of the message. A case-structure is used to parse the sub-ID #1 byte.

There is only one currently defined value for Real-Time SysEx sub-ID #1 — MTC (MIDI Time Code). A single-statement case-structure is used to parse the sub-ID #1 byte. Addtional case-statements can be added as other sub-ID #1s are defined. If sub-ID #1 is 1, an intermediate routine is called to parse the sub-ID #2 byte for the specific MTC message.

```
PROCEDURE ProcessRealSysEx;
BEGIN
  ReadMIDI(theMIDIByte);          {get device ID byte}
  IF SysExData = False THEN
    Exit(ProcessRealSysEx);       {stop if byte isn't data}

  IF (theMIDIByte <> 127) AND (theMIDIByte <> unitNumebr) THEN
    Exit(ProcessRealSysEx);       {stop if device ID s don't match}

  ReadMIDI(theMIDIByte);          {get sub-ID #1}
  IF SysExData = False THEN
    Exit(ProcessRealSysEx);       {stop if byte isn't data}

  CASE theMIDIByte OF             {parse sub-ID #1}
    1:
      ProcessMTC; {process MIDI TIME CODE}
    OTHERWISE
      ;{unrecognized Real Time sub-ID #, do nothing}
  END; {Case for sub-ID #1}
END; {ProcessRealSysEx}
```

MTC Messages

When this procedure is called, the next byte in the SysEx message (sub-ID #2) will indicate which of the two defined MTC messages to process. The byte is checked with SysExData. If it is a data byte, a case-structure is used to parse the byte. The routine to process the specified MTC message is called from the corresponding case-statement.

```
PROCEDURE ProcessMTC;
BEGIN
  ReadMIDI(theMIDIByte);          {get sub-ID #2}
  IF SysExData = False THEN
    Exit(ProcessMTC);             {stop if byte isn't data}

  CASE theMIDIByte OF             {parse sub-ID #2}
    1:
      GetFullMessage; {Full Message}
    2:
      GetUserBits; {User Bits}
    OTHERWISE
      ; {unrecognized MTC sub-ID #2, do nothing}
  END; {Case for sub-ID #2}
END;{ProcessMTC}
```

Processing SysEx Messages

In the previous section, we demonstrated a way to indentify and parse each type of System Exclusive message defined by MIDI. In this section, we'll demonstrate how to process messages of each type. By process, we mean to get and parse each byte of the specific message, decode any data that has been nibblized or encoded in some other manner, and store the decoded data values in an appropriate variable. It is our intention to show how to access the information contained in these messages. Any application that handles System Exclusive messages will need to do at least this much. How the information is manipulated, displayed, stored, etc. once it has been obtained, is up to you.

Decoding SysEx Data

SysEx messages are often used to convey values with more than seven significant bits. MIDI data bytes, by definition, have only seven significant bits. To transmit a value beyond this limit, the value must be encoded into two or more MIDI bytes. As these bytes are received, they must be decoded. There are two commonly used encode/decode formats: nibble formats and byte formats.

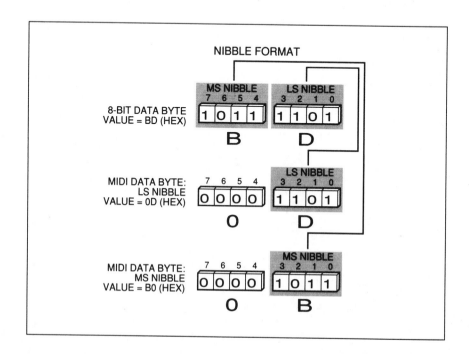

Nibble is a term for the lower or upper four bits of a byte. The LS nibble holds the four least-significant bits (bits 0-3), and the MS nibble holds the most significant bits (bits 4-7). Nibble formats transmit data one nibble (four bits) at a time. The LS nibble of a MIDI data byte carries the nibble of SysEx data. The bits in the MS nibble of the MIDI data byte are set to zero. This format is frequently used to transmit 8-bit values via MIDI. The MIDI bytes are sent in pairs with either the LS or MS nibble in the first byte, and the remaining bits in the second byte. In order to encode/decode nibblized data, you must know the transmission order (LS first or MS first) and the number of MIDI bytes per word.

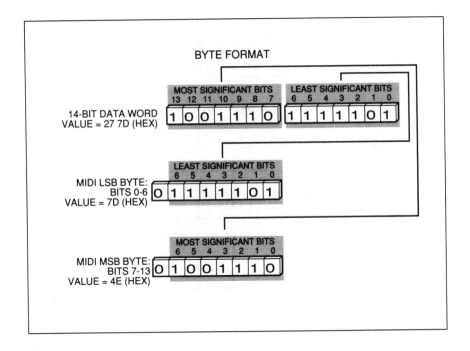

Byte formats are used to transmit values with eight or more significant bits. In this format, for example, a 12-bit value would be sent in two MIDI bytes. One would hold seven bits of the value and the other would hold the remaining five bits. A 16-bit value would be sent in three bytes. Two bytes would hold seven bits each, the third byte would hold the remaining two bits. The bytes are sent in series, starting with either the LS or MS byte. In order to encode/decode byte format data, you must know the number of bytes per word, and the transmission order (LS byte first or MS byte first).

The nibble formats (either LS or MS nibble first) are commonly used to transmit 8-bit values in SysEx messages. Of the byte formats, the LS byte first format is commonly used to transmit 2-byte (or larger) values in SysEx messages, and the MS byte first format is used to transmit the sample data values in the Sample Dump Data Packet message. Before we go on to designing routines to process specific SysEx messages, let's design some general purpose functions for decoding the data formats you're most likely to encounter.

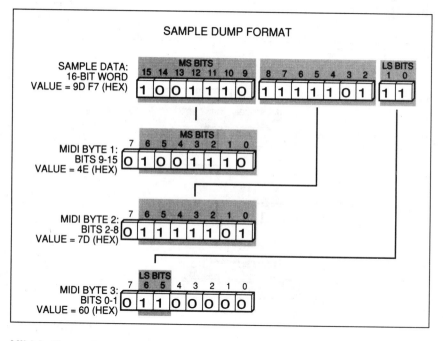

Nibble Formats

Here's a bare-bones function for decoding nibblized data sent LS nibble first. The decoding process consists of four steps:

1. Get the MIDI byte holding the LS nibble data (X).

2. Get the MIDI byte holding the MS nibble data (Y).

3. Shift the MS nibble data four bits to the left (This is the   same as multiplying by 16).

4. Add the LS value to the shifted MS value.

```
FUNCTION GetLSNFirst :integer;
  VAR
    X,Y : integer;
BEGIN
  ReadMIDI(X);            {get LS nibble}
  ReadMIDI(Y);            {get MS nibble}
  Y := BSL(Y,4);          {shift MS nibble 4 bits left}
  GetLSNFirst := X+Y;     {add LSN + MSN }
END; {GetLSNFirst}
```

A function for decoding nibblized data sent MS nibble first is almost identical. The only difference is that X is shifted this time, since the first byte received is the MS nibble.

```
FUNCTION GetMSNFirst :integer;
  VAR
    X,Y : integer;
BEGIN
  ReadMIDI(X);            {get MS nibble}
  X := BSL(Y,4);          {shift MS nibble 4 bits left}
  ReadMIDI(Y);            {get LS nibble}
  GetMSNFirst := X+Y;     {add MSN + LSN }
END; {GetMSNFirst}
```

Byte Formats

A function to decode a 2-byte, LS byte first value is given below. Like the nibblized formats, the decoding process consists of four steps:

1. Get the MIDI byte holding the LS byte data (X).

2. Get the MIDI byte holding the MS byte data (Y).

3. Shift the MS nibble data seven bits to the left (This is the same as multiplying by 128).

4. Add the LS value to the shifted MS value.

```
FUNCTION GetLSByteFirst :integer;
  VAR
    X,Y : integer;
BEGIN
  ReadMIDI(X);            {get LS byte}
  ReadMIDI(Y);            {get MS byte}
  Y := BSL(Y,7);          {shift MS byte 7 bits left}
  GetLSNFirst := X+Y;     {add LS + MS }
END; {GetLSNFirst}
```

The LS byte first format is frequently used to transmit values with more than 14 significant bits. This would require decoding an additional byte of MIDI data for each additional seven bits of resolution. Here's a more generalized LS byte first function that can decode any byte format values with up to 32 significant bits. The size variable holds the number of bytes to decode. The first step in this function is to assign the value of the LS byte to X. Then a for-loop is set up receive the remaining bytes and assign their running total in MSBits. Each time a byte is received in this loop, its value is shifted to the left by an offset and assigned to Y. The offset is initially set to 7, and increases by 7 with each additional byte. The first byte in the loop is shifted by 7, the next by 14, and so on. The value, Y, is added to the previous value of MSBits. After all of the remaining bytes have been received, shifted, and added, X and MSBits are added together. This sum is the decoded value of all of the bytes.

```
FUNCTION GetMSBytes (size: integer): longint;
  VAR
    X,Y Offset: integer;
    MSBits : longint;
BEGIN
  ReadMIDI(X);              {get LS byte}
  FOR Offset := 1 TO size - 1 DO
  BEGIN
    ReadMIDI(Y);            {get next byte}
    MSBits := MSBits + BSL(Y, 7 * Offset);{shift left 7bits and add}
  END;{For Offset ...}
  GetMSBytes := X + MSBits; {return MSbytes to calling routine}
END; {GetMSBytes}
```

Sample Dump Format

The data in Sample Dump Data Packet messages is encoded using an MS byte first format. In this case, the first byte received has the seven most significant bits, and the last byte received has the least significant bits. The total number of significant bits is transmitted as the "sample format" value in the Sample Dump Header message. This message is transmitted before the data packets are sent. We'll show you how to process that message later on, for now, keep in mind that this value will be stored in the "sFormat" field of a Pascal record we'll create to hold the infomation from the header message.

Following is another bare-bones function that shows how to decode sample dump data. Depending on the sample format value (which can be from 8 to 28 bits), there will be two, three, or four MIDI bytes of encoded data for each sample word. The first step in decoding sample dump data is to get this value. The value is obtained from a previously created record with a simple assignment statement:

```
shift := theDumpHdr.sformat;        {word size in bits}
```

The number of bits to shift each byte is determined as follows.

- Assign the sample format value to the shift variable

- Starting with the first byte to be decoded, reduce the shift value by 7. If the result is 7 or more, shift the byte to the left by that number, and add to the previous value of the word variable.

- Repeat this for each byte until the shift value becomes less than 7.

- If the shift value is zero, the MIDI byte holds the 7 LS bits of the value. Add this to the word value.

- If the shift value is greater than zero, the shift value is the number of bits that have to be decoded in the last byte. These bits are left-justified and will have to be shifted to the right. Subtract the shift value from seven and shift the byte to the right by the result. Add this value to the previous word value to obtain the decoded value of the sample word.

The shift variable is used as a control value in a while-structure. In the while-structure, bytes are received, shifted an appropriate number of bits to the left, and added to the word variable. For example, to shift the MS bits of a 16-bit data word, subtract 7 from 16 to get 9. On the first pass through the while-structure, the MS bits are shifted 9 places to the left. This puts bit 6-0 of the MIDI byte in bit 15-9 of the word variable. Next, the value of shift is decreased by seven. The next time through the while-structure, the calculation is repeated, this time subtracting 7 from 9 to get 2. The next byte is shifted two places to the left. This puts bits 6-0 of the MIDI data byte into bits 8-2 of the word variable . The shift value is now 2, and this causes the while-structure to stop. Since this value is also greater than zero, the final MIDI byte value must be shifted to the right. The number of places this byte must be shifted is calculated by subtracting the last value of shift from seven (7-2=5). The byte is shifted to the right 5 places and added to the word value.

```
FUNCTION GetSampleWord: longint;
  VAR
    X, Shift: integer;
    word: longint;
BEGIN
  word := 0;
  X := 0;
  shift := theDumpHdr.sformat; {get the word size in bits}

  WHILE (shift - 7) >= 7 DO
  BEGIN
    ReadMIDI(X);                    {get a byte}
    word := word + BSL(X, shift - 7); {shift left and add}
    shift := shift - 7;  {set the shift value for the next byte}
  END;

  ReadMIDI(X);                      {get last byte}
  IF shift > 0 THEN                 {if less than 7 bits remain}
    X := BSR(X, shift);             {shift right to LS bit}
  GetSampleWord := word + X;        {add MS bits and last byte}
END;{GetSampleWord}
```

Decoding Functions for SysEx Examples

As nibblized and LS byte formats are used so frequently in SysEx messages, we'll create a single function to call whenever it's necessary to decode any of these formats. We'll declare four constants — one for each of three decoding "modes," and one to flag decode errors.

```
CONST
    LSNibbleMode = 0;      {decode mode 0: 2 bytes LS Nibble first}
    MSNibbleMode = 1;      {decode mode 1: 2 bytes MS Nibble first}
    LSByteMode = 2;        {decode mode 2: dataSize bytes LS Byte first}
    DecodeERROR = $FFFFFFFF;   {decode error}
```

When the function is called, the value of its mode parameter determines which decoding algorithm is used. If the LS byte mode is selected, the function's size parameter holds the number of bytes to decode. The code within the function is based on the algorithms used in the previous decoding functions. Error checking calls to SysExData have been included every time a new MIDI byte is received. If an error is detected this function will flag the calling routine with a decodeERROR. It is the calling routine's responsibility to check for and respond to the decodeERROR.

```
FUNCTION DecodeData (size, mode: integer): longint;
  VAR
    X, Y, Offset: integer;
    word: longint;
BEGIN
  ReadMIDI(X);                           {get byte 1}
  IF SysExData = False THEN              {if it's not data,}
    DecodeData := DecodeERROR            {set decode error flag}
  ELSE
  BEGIN
    CASE mode OF
      LSNibbleMode:
      BEGIN
        Y := GetMSNibble;               {get and shift MS Nibble}
        IF Y = DecodeERROR THEN         {if it's not data}
          DecodeData := DecodeERROR     {set decode error flag}
        ELSE
          DecodeData := X + Y;          {combine LS and MS nibbles}
      END; {LS Nibble}

      MSNibbleMode:
      BEGIN
        ReadMIDI(Y);                    {get byte with LS Nibble}
        IF SysExData = False THEN       {if it's not data,}
          DecodeData := DecodeERROR     {set decode error flag}
        ELSE
        BEGIN
          X := BSL(X, 4);               {shift MS Nibble}
          DecodeData := X + Y;          {combine LS and MS nibbles}
        END;
      END; {MS Nibble}

      LSByteMode:
      BEGIN
        word := GetMSBytes(size);
        IF word = DecodeERROR THEN      {if it's not data}
          DecodeData := DecodeERROR     {set decode error flag}
        ELSE
          DecodeData := X + Word;{combine LS and MS bytes}
      END; {LSByte}
    END;{Case mode...}
  END;{X is data}
END;{DecodeData}
```

When decoding LS nibble first data, DecodeData calls the function, GetMSNibble, to input and shift the byte containing the MS nibble data.

```
FUNCTION GetMSNibble: longInt;
  VAR
    Y: integer;
BEGIN
  ReadMIDI(Y);                          {get byte with MS Nibble}
  IF SysExData = False THEN             {if it's not data,}
    GetMSNibble := DecodeERROR          {set decode error flag}
  ELSE
  BEGIN
    Y := BSL(Y, 4);                     {shift left 4 bits}
    GetMSNibble := Y;
  END;
END; {GetMSNibble}
```

When decoding LS byte data, DecodeData calls the function, GetMSbyte, to input and shift the bytes containing the MS data.

```
FUNCTION GetMSBytes (size: integer): longint;
  VAR
    Y, Offset: integer;
    MSBits :longint;
BEGIN
  FOR Offset := 1 TO Size - 1 DO
  BEGIN
    ReadMIDI(Y);                        {get next byte}
    IF SysExData = False THEN           {if it's not data,}
    BEGIN
      GetMSBytes := DecodeERROR;{set decode error flag}
      Exit(GetMSBytes);                 {return to calling routine}
    END
    ELSE
      MSBits := MSBits+ BSL(Y, 7 * Offset);{shift left 7 bits,and add}
  END;{For Offset ...}
  GetMSBytes := MSBits;                 {return to calling routine}
END; {GetMSBytes}
```

Here is function that can decode sample data words of any size, from 8-28 bits. Based on the previous MSByte procedure, this version also checks each incoming byte to make sure it is valid data. If an error is detected, this function will flag the calling routine with a decodeERROR. It is the calling routine's responsibility to check for and respond to the decodeERROR.

```
FUNCTION GetSampleWord: longint;
  VAR
    X, Shift: integer;
    word: longint;
BEGIN
  word := 0;
  X := 0;
  shift := theDumpHdr.sformat;          {word size in bits}

  WHILE shift - 7 >= 7 DO
  BEGIN
    ReadMIDI(X);                        {get a byte}
    IF SysExData = False THEN
    BEGIN
      GetSampleWord := DecodeERROR;
      Exit(GetSampleWord);
    END;
    word := word + BSL(X, shift - 7);   {shift left and add}
    shift := shift - 7;
  END;
  ReadMIDI(X);                          {get last byte}
  IF SysExData = False THEN
  BEGIN
    GetSampleWord := DecodeERROR;
    Exit(GetSampleWord);
  END;
  IF shift > 0 THEN                     {if less than 7 bits remain}
    X := BSR(X, shift);                 {shift right to LS bit}
  GetSampleWord := word + X;            {add MS bits and last byte}
END; {GetSampleWord}
```

Processing Manufacturer ID SysEx Messages

Now that we have procedures that can parse SysEx message types, and functions that can decode the data they contain, we can put together some routines that demonstrate how to process specific messages.

Our SysEx processing shell example is developed to the point where it can recognize messages intended for any specific manufacturer. Now it's time to add routines that can recognize and process specific Manufacturer ID SysEx messages. All manufacturers have their own SysEx formats, so a different set of routines must be developed for each manufacturer and device. Although they differ in specifics, most SysEx formats are pretty similar. The formats used by a specific device should be published in its user documentation. We'll use the Parameter Change message transmitted by the Korg M1 MIDI workstation for the following examples. You'll find the general techniques employed in the examples can be easily applied to other MIDI devices made by Korg or other manufacturers.

All Korg SysEx messages transmitted/recognized by the M1 have the following format.

Byte	Hex	Binary	Description
1	F0	1111 0000	SysEx status
2	42	0100 0010	Korg ID
3	3n	0011 nnnn	Format ID :global channel
4	19	0001 1001	M1 ID
5	ff	0fff ffff	function code
6	dd	0ddd dddd	first data byte
		.	
		.	any number of data bytes
		.	
n	dd	0ddd dddd	last data byte
n+1	F7	1111 0111	EOX

The previously described procedure, ProcessSysEx, parses byte 2 of all SysEx messages and calls ProcessKorgSysEx if the value of the byte is the Korg ID (42H). ProcessKorgSysEx will have to parse the third, fourth, and fifth bytes of the message to determine which specific M1 message processing procedure to call. Byte 4 of the message identifies it as one intended for the M1. Byte 5 of the message identifies the specific M1 message type. The function codes are given in the following table.

Function Code	Message
21H	Write Completed
22H	Write Error
23H	Data Load Completed
24H	Data Load Error
26H	Received Message Format Error
40H	Program Parameter Jump
41H	Parameter Change
42H	Mode Data
45H	All Multi-Sound
47H	All Drum Sound
48H	All Sequence Data Dump
49H	Combination Parameter Jump
4DH	All Combination Parameter Jump
4EH	Mode Change
50H	All Data Dump
51H	Global Data Dump

We'll design a procedure to process the M1 Parameter Change message (function code 41H). The format of this message looks like this:

Byte	Hex	Binary	Description
1	F0	1111 0000	SysEx status
2	42	0100 0010	Korg ID
3	3n	0011 nnnn	Format ID: global channel
4	19	0001 1001	M1 ID
5	41	0100 0001	Parameter Change
6	pp	0ppp pppp	parameter page
7	0p	0000 pppp	parameter position
8	dd	0ddd dddd	value LSB (bits 6-0)
9	dd	0ddd dddd	value MSB (bits 13-7)
10	F7	1111 0111	EOX

Here are the declarations for global variables used by our routines.

```
CONST
{Constants for Korg M1 SysEx headers}
    KorgID = $42;              {byte 2: Korg ID}
    KorgFormatID = $30;        {byte 3: format ID}
    M1_ID = $19;               {byte 4:device ID (M1)}
    ParameterChange = $41; {byte 5: parameter change message}

  TYPE
    M1ParameterData = RECORD
        page: 0..127;
        position: 0..15;
        value: longint;
      END;

  VAR
    theM1Parameter: M1ParameterData;      {holds M1 parameter value}
```

The following procedure, ProcessKorgSysEx gets the next three bytes of a Korg SysEx message to determine if the message is an M1 message. If so, a case-structure is used to parse the function code (byte 5) to call the appropriate, message-specific processing procedure. A case-statement is included for each recognized M1 message. In our example, only the Parameter Change message (41H) is recognized.

```
PROCEDURE ProcessKorgSysEx;
BEGIN
  ReadMIDI(theMIDIByte);              {get Korg format ID}
  IF (SysExData = False) OR (theMIDIBYTE <> KorgFormatID) THEN
    Exit(ProcessKorgSysEx);           {stop if not Korg format ID}

  ReadMIDI(theMIDIByte);              {get M1_ID}
  IF (SysExData = False) OR (theMIDIBYTE <> M1_ID) THEN
    Exit(ProcessKorgSysEx);           {stop if not M1_ID}

  ReadMIDI(theMIDIByte);              {get M1 function code}
  IF SysExData = False THEN
    Exit(ProcessKorgSysEx);           {stop if byte isn't data}


  CASE theMIDIByte OF                 {M1 function code}

    $21..$24, $26:
      ; {handshaking messages}
    $40:
      ; {program dump}
    $41: Parameter Change
      GetM1ParameterChange;
    $42:
      ; {mode data}
    $45:
      ; {all multi sound(PCM Card)name}
    $47:
      ; {all drum sound(PCM Card)name}
    $48:
      ; {all sequence data dump}
    $49:
      ; {combination parameter dump}
    $50:
      ;{all data (GLB,CMB,PRG,SEQ) dump}
    $51:
      ; {global data dump}
    OTHERWISE
      ; {unrecognized M1 function code, report error}
  END; {Case for function code}
END;{ProcessKorgSysEx}
```

The following procedure shows how to process the M1 Parameter Change message. The message values are read and placed in a Pascal record. This simulates inserting them into a voice edit buffer or similar data structure. (Depending on your particular application, you can manipulate these values any number of ways.) Note the use of the decoding function, decodeData, to obtain a single value from LSB and MSB bytes.

```
PROCEDURE GetM1ParameterChange;
  VAR
    dataWord: longint;

BEGIN
  WITH theM1Parameter DO
  BEGIN
    ReadMIDI(theMIDIByte);              {get page}
    IF SysExData = False THEN
      Exit(GetM1ParameterChange);       {stop if not data}
    page := theMIDIByte;

    ReadMIDI(theMIDIByte);              {get position}
    IF SysExData = False THEN
      Exit(GetM1ParameterChange);       {stop if not data}
    position := theMIDIByte;

    dataWord := DecodeData(2, LSbyteMode);
    IF value = decodeERROR THEN
      Exit(GetM1ParameterChange);
    value := dataWord;
  END;
END; {GetM1ParameterChange}
```

Processing Non-Real-Time SysEx Messages

Non-Real-Time SysEx messages are parsed according to type in ProcessNon-RealSysEx. There are four types: Sample Dump, Sample Dump Extension, MTC Setup, and Device Inquiry. The messages are parsed according to the value of the sub-ID #1 and sub-ID #2 bytes. Sample Dump messages don't have a sub-ID #2 byte and the procedures for processing them are called directly from ProcessNonRealSysEx. Of the remaining types, each has more than one message, so intermediate procedures are called to parse messages of each type. The code for ProcessNonRealSysEx is repeated below.

```
PROCEDURE ProcessNonRealSysEx;
BEGIN
  ReadMIDI(theMIDIByte);          {get device ID byte}
  IF SysExData = False THEN
    Exit(ProcessNonRealSysEx);  {stop if byte isn't data}

  IF (theMIDIByte <> 127) AND (theMIDIByte <> unitNumber) THEN
    Exit(ProcessNonRealSysEx);  {stop if device IDs don't match}

  ReadMIDI(theMIDIByte);          {get sub-ID #1}
  IF SysExData = False THEN
    Exit(ProcessNonRealSysEx);  {stop if byte isn't data}

  CASE theMIDIByte OF             {parse sub-ID #1}
    1:
      GetSDHeader; {process SD Header}
    2:
      ; {process SD Data Packet}
    3:
      ; {process SD Request}
    4:
      ProcessMTCSetUp; {process MIDI TIME CODE messages}
    5:
      ProcessSDExt; {process SAMPLE DUMP EXTENSION messages}
    6:
      ProcessDevInquiry; {process DEVICE INQUIRY messages}
    $7C:
      ; {process Wait}
    $7D:
      ; {process Cancel}
    $7E:
      ; {process ACK}
    $7F:
      ; {process NAK}
    OTHERWISE
      ;{unrecognized sub-ID #1, do nothing}
  END; {Case for Non-Real-Time sub-ID #1}
END; {ProcessNonRealSysEx}
```

Sample Dump Messages

In our example, routines for each of the sample dump messages are called directly from ProcessNonRealSysEx. In a real application, these routines should be called from with a procedure that implements either the open or closed loop Sample Dump Standard communication protocol. (See page 127.) Our intention here is only to demonstrate the way in which a message would be processed, so we have not included any handshaking logic in the example. We chose the Sample Dump Header message, as it contains all of the specific information relating to a particular sampled sound. As with other SysEx messages, it is usually necessary to create a data structure to hold the values of the message. In this case, we set up a record to hold the sample number, loop type, sample format, sample period, sample length, and sustain loop points.

```
TYPE
    SDumpHdr = RECORD        {record to hold sample dump header values}
        sNumber, loopType: integer;
        sFormat, sPeriod, sLength, susStart, susEnd: longint
    END;

VAR
    theDumpHdr: SDumpHdr;   {holds dump header values}
```

The processing procedure, GetSDHeader, is called directly from ProcessNon-RealSysEx. It uses the decodeData function to retrieve the 2-byte and 3-byte values contained in the message. As each value is received, it is checked to see if it is a legal data value. If an error occurred during the decoding process, decodeData sets the value to decodeERROR. If an error is detected, processing stops, and control returns to the calling routine. If no error occurred during decoding, the value is placed in the appropriate field of the record, theDumpHdr.

```
PROCEDURE GetSDHeader;
  VAR
    dataWord: longInt;
BEGIN
  WITH theDumpHdr DO
  BEGIN
    dataWord := DecodeData(2, LSbyteMode);{get sample number (2 bytes)}
    IF dataWord = decodeERROR THEN
      Exit(GetSDHeader);            {stop if word isn't valid data}
    sNumber := dataWord; {load value into dhdr record}

    ReadMIDI(theMIDIByte);         {get sample format (1 byte)}
    IF SysExData = False THEN
      Exit(GetSDHeader);
    sFormat := theMIDIByte;

    dataWord := DecodeData(3, LSbyteMode);{get sample period (3 bytes)}
    IF dataWord = decodeERROR THEN
      Exit(GetSDHeader);
    sPeriod := dataWord;

    dataWord := DecodeData(3, LSbyteMode);{get sample length (3 bytes)}
    IF dataWord = decodeERROR THEN
      Exit(GetSDHeader);
    sLength := dataWord;

    dataWord := DecodeData(3, LSbyteMode);{get sus loop start (3 bytes)}
    IF dataWord = decodeERROR THEN
      Exit(GetSDHeader);
    susStart := dataWord;

    dataWord := DecodeData(2, LSbyteMode);{get sus loop end (3 bytes)}
    IF dataWord = decodeERROR THEN
      Exit(GetSDHeader);
    susEnd := dataWord;

    ReadMIDI(theMIDIByte);              {get loop type (1 byte)}
    IF SysExData = False THEN
      Exit(GetSDHeader);
    loopType := theMIDIByte;
  END;
END;{GetSDHeader}
```

Setup Messages

ProcessMTCSetup is an intermediate procedure called from ProcessNon-RealSysEx. It is called whenever an MTC Set-Up message arrives. It parses sub-ID #2 and calls the processing routine for the corresponding set-up type. A case-structure is used, with a case-statement for each recognized set-up type. Our example recognizes types 3 and 4, Punch In Time, and Punch Out Time.

```
PROCEDURE ProcessMTCSetUp;
BEGIN
  ReadMIDI(theMIDIByte);          {get sub-ID #2}
  IF SysExData = False THEN
    Exit(ProcessMTCSetUp);        {stop if byte isn't data}

  CASE theMIDIByte OF             {parse sub-ID #2}
    0:
      ;{Special}
    1, 2:
      GetPunchTime(theMIDIByte); {Punch In/Out}
    3, 4:
      ; {Delete Punch In/Out}
    5, 6:
      ; {Event Start/Stop}
    7, 8:
      ; {Event Start/Stop + Info}
    9, $A:
      ; {Delete Event Start/Stop}
    $B:
      ; {Cue Points}
    $C:
      ;{Cue Points + Info}
    $D:
      ;{Delete Cue Points}
    $E:
      ;{Event Name in Info}
    OTHERWISE
      ; {unrecognized MTC sub-ID #2, do nothing}
  END; {Case for sub-ID #2}
END;{ProcessMTCSetUp}
```

Most of the MTC Set-Up messages carry a set of SMPTE Time fields for frames, fractional frames, hours, minutes, and seconds, as well as an event number. We set up a record to hold these values. The record also holds the event type.

```
TYPE
    SmpteEvent = RECORD              {record to hold MTC Set-Up event values}
        frame: 0..29;
        fracFrames: 0..99;
        seconds: 0..60;
        minutes: 0..59;
        hours: 0..23;
        TimeCodeType: 0..3;
        eventNumber: longint;
        eventType: 0..$0E;
    END;


VAR
    theSmpteEvent: SmpteEvent; {holds MTC Set-Up values (but not +info)}
```

GetPunchTime demonstrates how to process any of the set up messages. Each value is retrieved, checked, and stored in the record. Note that this procedure is used to process both Punch In and Punch Out messages. The event type field in the record specifies if the SMPTE time is for Punch in or Punch out.

```
PROCEDURE GetPunchTime (punchType: integer);
  VAR
    dataWord: longint;
    X: integer;

BEGIN
  WITH theSmpteEvent DO
  BEGIN
    eventType := punchType;      {get punch In/Out type}

    ReadMIDI(theMIDIByte);       {get hour/type (1 byte)}
    IF SysExData = False THEN
      Exit(GetPunchTime);
    X := theMIDIByte;
    hours := BitAND(X, $1F);     {decode & store hours }
    TimeCodeType := BSR(theMIDIByte, 5); {decode & store TC type }
```

```
      ReadMIDI(theMIDIByte);        {get minutes (1 byte)}
      IF SysExData = False THEN
        Exit(GetPunchTime);
      minutes := theMIDIByte;

      ReadMIDI(theMIDIByte);        {get seconds (1 byte)}
      IF SysExData = False THEN
        Exit(GetPunchTime);
      seconds := theMIDIByte;

      ReadMIDI(theMIDIByte);        {get frame (1 byte)}
      IF SysExData = False THEN
        Exit(GetPunchTime);
      frame := theMIDIByte;

      ReadMIDI(theMIDIByte);        {get fractional frames (1 byte)}
      IF SysExData = False THEN
        Exit(GetPunchTime);
      fracFrames := theMIDIByte;

      dataWord := DecodeData(2, LSbyteMode);{get event number (2 bytes)}
      IF dataWord = decodeERROR THEN
        Exit(GetPunchTime);
      eventNumber := dataWord;
    END;
END; {GetPunchTime}
```

Sample Dump Extension Messages

ProcessSDExt is an intermediate procedure called from ProcessNonReal-
SysEx. It is called whenever a Sample Dump Extension message arrives. It
uses a case-structure to parse the sub-ID #2 byte of the message and to call
the processing procedure for the corresponding message. Our example recognizes the Multiple Loop Points message.

```
PROCEDURE ProcessSDExt;
BEGIN
  ReadMIDI(theMIDIByte);          {get sub-ID #2}
  IF SysExData = False THEN
    Exit(ProcessSDExt);           {stop if byte isn't data}

  CASE theMIDIByte OF             {parse sub-ID #2}
    1:
      GetLoopPoints;
    2:
      ; {Loop Points Request}

    OTHERWISE
      ; {unrecognized SD Extension sub-ID #2, do nothing}
  END; {Case for sub-ID #2}
END;{ProcessSDExt}
```

The Loop Points message carries the loop number, type, and start and end
points for a given sample number. As in our previous examples, we set up
a record to hold these values.

```
TYPE
  LoopPointData = RECORD {record to hold sample dump header values}
    sNumber, loopNumber, loopType: integer;
    loopStart, loopEnd: longint
  END;

VAR
  theLoop: LoopPointData;{holds loop point data values}
```

GetLoopPoint retrieves, decodes, and checks each value in the message. The decoded values are placed into the appropriate fields of the record, theLoop.

```
PROCEDURE GetLoopPoint;
  VAR
    dataWord: longint;
BEGIN
  BEGIN
    WITH theLoop DO
    BEGIN
      dataWord := DecodeData(2, LSbyteMode); {get s number (2 bytes)}
      IF dataWord = decodeERROR THEN
        Exit(GetLoopPoint);
      sNumber := dataWord;

      dataWord := DecodeData(2, LSbyteMode); {get l number (2 bytes)}
      IF dataWord = decodeERROR THEN
        Exit(GetLoopPoint);
      loopNumber := dataWord;

      ReadMIDI(theMIDIByte);                 {get loop type (1 byte)}
      IF SysExData = False THEN
        Exit(GetLoopPoint);
      loopType := theMIDIByte;

      dataWord := DecodeData(3, LSbyteMode); {get loop start (3 bytes)}
      IF dataWord = decodeERROR THEN
        Exit(GetLoopPoint);
      loopStart := dataWord;

      dataWord := DecodeData(2, LSbyteMode); {get loop end (3 bytes)}
      IF dataWord = decodeERROR THEN
        Exit(GetLoopPoint);
      loopEnd := dataWord;
    END;
  END; {Case theMIDIByte}
END; {GetLoopPoint}
```

Device Inquiry Messages

ProcessDevInquiry is called from ProcessNonRealSysEx whenever a Device Inquiry message is received. A case-structure is used to parse the value of sub-ID #2. A separate case-statement is used for each of the two Device Inquiry messages currently defined. Our example recognizes the Device ID Response message.

```
PROCEDURE ProcessDevInquiry;
BEGIN
  ReadMIDI(theMIDIByte);          {get sub-ID #2}
  IF SysExData = False THEN
    Exit(ProcessDevInquiry);      {stop if byte isn't data}

  CASE theMIDIByte OF             {parse sub-ID #2}
    1:
      ; {Device ID Request}
    2:
      GetDeviceID;
    OTHERWISE
      ; {unrecognized Device Inquiry sub-ID #2, do nothing}
  END; {Case for sub-ID #2}
END;{ProcessDevInquiry}
```

For our example, we'll only recognize ID responses from Korg instruments. A Korg ID response contains the Korg ID, family code, member, ROM number, and software version. A record is created to hold the values of a Korg's Device ID response.

```
TYPE
  KorgDevID = RECORD
      familyCode, memberCode, ROMCode, softVersion: integer;
    END;

VAR
  theKorgDevice: KorgDevID;
```

GetDeviceID uses a case-structure to parse the manufacturer ID byte in the message. A separate case-statement is used for each recognized manufacturer. Our example only recognizes Korg ID responses. If a Korg message is received, each value is retrieved, decoded (if necessary) and checked before placing it into the appropriate record field.

```
PROCEDURE  GetDeviceID;
BEGIN
  ReadMIDI(theMIDIByte);              {Manufacturer ID (1 byte)}
  IF SysExData = False THEN
    Exit(GetDeviceID);

  CASE theMIDIByte OF
    KorgID:                           {only interested in Korg IDs}
    BEGIN
      WITH theKorgDevice DO
      BEGIN
        familyCode := DecodeData(2, LSbyteMode);{getfamily (2 bytes)}
        IF familyCode = decodeERROR THEN
          Exit(GetDeviceID);

        memberCode := DecodeData(2, LSbyteMode);{get member (2 bytes)}
        IF memberCode = decodeERROR THEN
          Exit(GetDeviceID);

        ROMCode := DecodeData(2, LSbyteMode);{get ROM No. (2 bytes)}
        IF ROMCode = decodeERROR THEN
          Exit(GetDeviceID);

        softVersion := DecodeData(2, LSbyteMode);{get softVer.(2 bytes)}
        IF softVersion = decodeERROR THEN
          Exit(GetDeviceID);
      END; {with the KorgDevice}
    END; {KorgID}

    OTHERWISE
      ; {manufacturer ID not recognized by application}
  END; {Case theMIDIByte}
END;{GetDeviceID}
```

Processing Real-Time MTC SysEx Messages

In ProcessRealTSysEx, Real-Time SysEx messages are parsed according to type. There is currently only one defined Real-Time SysEx type. We set up a case-structure so that types defined in the future can be added to the procedure. The code for ProcessRealSysEx is repeated below.

```
PROCEDURE ProcessRealSysEx;
BEGIN
  ReadMIDI(theMIDIByte);          {get device ID byte}
  IF SysExData = False THEN
    Exit(ProcessRealSysEx);       {stop if byte isn't data}

  IF (theMIDIByte <> 127) AND (theMIDIByte <> unitNumber) THEN
    Exit(ProcessRealSysEx);       {stop if device IDs don't match}

  ReadMIDI(theMIDIByte);          {get sub-ID #1}
  IF SysExData = False THEN
    Exit(ProcessRealSysEx);       {stop if byte isn't data}

  CASE theMIDIByte OF             {parse sub-ID #1}
    1:
      ProcessMTC; {process MIDI TIME CODE}
    OTHERWISE
      ;{unrecognized Real Time sub-ID #1, do nothing}
  END; {Case for sub-ID #1}
END; {ProcessRealSysEx}
```

ProcessMTC is an intermediate procedure called from ProcessRealSysEx. It uses a case-structure to parse the sub-ID #2 byte and call the appropriate MIDI Time Code message. Our example recognizes the two messages currently defined — Full Message and User Bits.

```
PROCEDURE ProcessMTC;
BEGIN
  ReadMIDI(theMIDIByte);          {get sub-ID #2}
  IF SysExData = False THEN
    Exit(ProcessMTC);             {stop if byte isn't data}

  CASE theMIDIByte OF             {parse sub-ID #2}
    1:
      GetFullMessage; {Full Message}
    2:
      GetUserBits; {User Bits}
    OTHERWISE
      ; {unrecognized MTC sub-ID #2, do nothing}
  END; {Case for sub-ID #2}
END;{ProcessMTC}
```

Full Message

The MTC Full message is used to transmit a SMPTE time to "auto-locate" an MTC device. The SMPTE time consists of values for hours, minutes, seconds, and frames. The time code type is also sent in the message. A record is created to hold each of these values.

```
TYPE

    SmpteTime  =  RECORD          {record to hold MTC Full Message time fields}

                  hours: 0..23;

                  minutes: 0..59;

                  seconds: 0..60;

                  frame: 0..29;
```

```
                    TimeCodeType: 0..3;

            END;

VAR

   theSmpteTime: SmpteTime;        {holds MTC Full Message time}
```

GetFullMessage demonstrates how to process the Full Message. Each SMPTE value is retrieved, checked, and stored in the appropriate record field.

```
PROCEDURE GetFullMessage;
  VAR
    X: integer;

BEGIN
  WITH theSmpteTime DO
  BEGIN
    ReadMIDI(theMIDIByte);        {get hour/type}
    IF SysExData = False THEN
      Exit(GetFullMessage);
    X := theMIDIByte;
    hours := BitAND(X, $1F);      {decode & store hours }
    TimeCodeType := BSR(theMIDIByte, 5); {decode & store TC type }

    ReadMIDI(theMIDIByte);        {get minutes }
    IF SysExData = False THEN
      Exit(GetFullMessage);
    minutes := theMIDIByte;

    ReadMIDI(theMIDIByte);        {get seconds}
    IF SysExData = False THEN
      Exit(GetFullMessage);
```

```
        seconds := theMIDIByte;

        ReadMIDI(theMIDIByte);        {get frame }
        IF SysExData = False THEN
          Exit(GetFullMessage);
        frame := theMIDIByte;
    END;
  END;{GetFullMessage}
```

User Bits Message

The User Bits message is used to transmit four 8-bit characters and two bit-flags used by SMPTE devices. A record is created to hold each of these values.

```
TYPE
    userBits = RECORD        {record to hold SMPTE User Bits and Bit-Flags}

            user1, user2, user3, user4: integer;
            userFlag1, userFlag2: boolean;
            END;

        VAR
            theUserBits: userBits; {holds MTC user bits data}
```

GetUserBits demonstrates how to process the User Bits message. Each of the four characters is retrieved, decoded, and checked. (Note the use of the MS nibble mode.) The flag values are decoded by testing the specific bit location in the data word with the BTST function. It evalutes true if the bit is set, and false if the bit is clear.

```
PROCEDURE GetUserBits;
  VAR
    X: integer;
BEGIN
  WITH theUserBits DO
  BEGIN
    X := DecodeData(2, MSNibbleMode); {get user char 1 (2 bytes)}
    IF X = decodeERROR THEN
      Exit(GetUserBits);
    user1 := X;

    X := DecodeData(2, MSNibbleMode); {get user char 2 (2 bytes)}
    IF X = decodeERROR THEN
      Exit(GetUserBits);
    user2 := X;

    X := DecodeData(2, MSNibbleMode); {get user char 3 (2 bytes)}
    IF X = decodeERROR THEN
      Exit(GetUserBits);
    user3 := X;

    X := DecodeData(2, MSNibbleMode); {get user char 4 (2 bytes)}
    IF X = decodeERROR THEN
      Exit(GetUserBits);
    user4 := X;
```

Appendix

MIDI Programming Examples

Appendix

MIDI Programming Examples

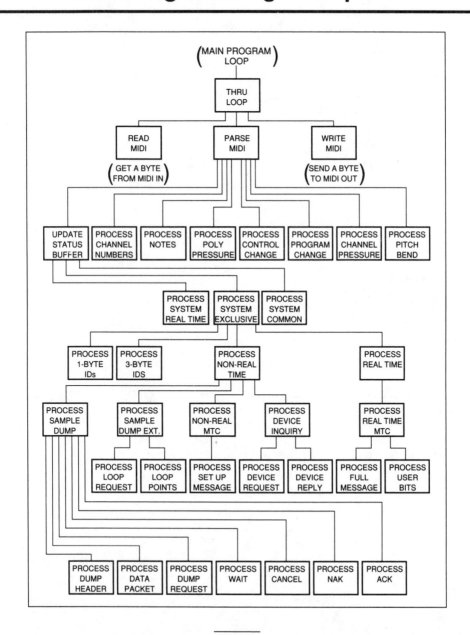

```
{File Name:MIDIRoutines                              }
{Description:example routines for parsing and processing MIDI data}
{Original Date : 8/8/89                    By: SDF      }


UNIT MIDIThruProcs;
INTERFACE


  CONST
  {range limits for each status type}
    NoteOff1 = $80;           {NoteOff/Channel 1}
    NoteOff16 = $8F; {NoteOff/Channel 16}
    NoteOn1 = $90;            {etc. ....}
    NoteOn16 = $9F;
    PolyPress1 = $A0;
    PolyPress16 = $AF;
    ControlChange1 = $B0;
    ControlChange16 = $BF;
    ProgramChange1 = $C0;
    ProgramChange16 = $CF;
    ChanPress1 = $D0;
    ChanPress16 = $DF;
    PitchWheel1 = $E0;
    PitchWheel16 = $EF;
    TimingClock = $F8;
    SystemReset = $FF;
    SysEx = $F0;              {lowest System Common status value}
    QFrame = $F1;             {MTC Quarter Frame Message}
    EOX = $F7;                {highest System Common status value}

{Constants for Korg M1 SysEx headers}
    KorgID = $42;          {byte 2: Korg ID}
    KorgFormatID = $30;    {byte 3: format ID}
    M1_ID = $19;           {byte 4:device ID (M1)}
    ParameterChange = $41;{byte 5: parameter change message}
```

```
  Ignore = 0;               {flag for unrecognized status}
  FilterOn = False;         {filter is on, don't pass data}
  FilterOff = True;{filter is off, process and pass data}

  DecodeERROR = $FFFFFFFF;{status rcv'd when data expected}
  LSNibbleMode = 0;         {decode mode 0: 2 bytes LS Nibble first}
  MSNibbleMode = 1;         {decode mode 1: 2 bytes MS Nibble first}
  LSByteMode = 2; {decode mode 2: dataSize bytes LS Byte first}

TYPE
  KorgDevID = RECORD
      familyCode, memberCode, ROMCode, softVersion: integer;
    END;

  M1ParameterData = RECORD
      page: 0..127;
      position: 0..15;
      value: longint;
    END;

  SDumpHdr = RECORD       {record holds sample dump header values}
      sNumber, loopType: integer;
      sFormat, sPeriod, sLength, susStart, susEnd: longint
    END;

  LoopPointData = RECORD {record holds sample dump header values}
      sNumber, loopNumber, loopType: integer;
      loopStart, loopEnd: longint
    END;

  SmpteEvent = RECORD {record holds MTC Setup event values}
      frame: 0..29;
      fracFrames: 0..99;
      seconds: 0..60;
      minutes: 0..59;
      hours: 0..23;
      TimeCodeType: 0..3;
      eventNumber: longint;
      eventType: 0..$0E;
    END;
```

```
SmpteTime = RECORD {record holds MTC Full Message time fields}
    hours: 0..23;
    minutes: 0..59;
    seconds: 0..60;
    frame: 0..29;
    TimeCodeType: 0..3;
  END;

userBits = RECORD {to hold SMPTE User Bits and Bit Flags}
    user1, user2, user3, user4: integer;
    userFlag1, userFlag2: boolean;
  END;

VAR
  theMIDIByte: Integer; {byte received from your MIDI In routine}
  statusBuffer: Integer; {to hold last received status value}
  dataCount: Integer;    {counts order data bytes received}
  ThruFlag: Boolean;     {used to turn Thru Loop On/Off}

  NoteFlag: Boolean;     {to turn processing routines on/off}
  PPressFlag: Boolean;   {each message type}
  CCHangeFlag: Boolean;
  PChangeFlag: Boolean;
  CPressFlag: Boolean;
  PWheelFlag: Boolean;
  ChannelFlag: Boolean;

  myDevID: integer;      {device ID of this program}
  devID: integer; {device  ID in Universal SysEx messages}
  SysExFlag: Boolean;    {turns SysEx processing on/off}

  dataSize: integer; {number of bytes in a word to be decoded}
  bytes, bits: integer; {number of bytes/bits in sample data}

  Channel: ARRAY[0..15] OF integer;{holds ch reassignment values}
  theDumpHdr: SDumpHdr;            {holds dump header values}
  theLoop: LoopPointData;         {holds loop point data values}
  theSmpteEvent: SmpteEvent; {holds MTC Setup values-not +info)}
  theSmpteTime: SmpteTime;        {holds MTC Full Message time}
  theUserBits: userBits;          {holds MTC user bits data}
  theM1Parameter: M1ParameterData;{holds Korg M1 parameter vals}
  theKorgDevice: KorgDevID;
```

```
IMPLEMENTATION

{————————————————————}
  PROCEDURE UpdateStatus;
  forward;

{————————————————————}
  PROCEDURE ReadMIDI (byte: integer);
  BEGIN
    ;{use any routine that returns a MIDI Byte from MIDI In}
  END;{ReadMIDI}

{————————————————————}
  PROCEDURE WriteMIDI (byte: integer);
  BEGIN
    ;{use any routine that sends a MIDI Byte to MIDI Out}
  END;{WriteMIDI}

{————————————————————}
  FUNCTION GetChannel (byte: integer): integer;
    VAR
      X: integer;
  BEGIN
    X := BitAND(byte, $F0);
    GetChannel := X;
  END;{GetChannel}

{————————————————————}
  FUNCTION SysExData: Boolean;
  BEGIN
    CASE theMIDIByte OF
      $0..$7F:      {byte was data, tell calling}
        SysExData := True; {routine it's OK to process}

      NoteOff1..EOX: {byte was status byte,}
      BEGIN
        UpdateStatus;{update status buffer}
        SysExData := False; {warn the calling routine}
      END;

      TimingClock..SystemReset:   {byte was Real-Time,}
      BEGIN
        ReadMIDI(theMIDIByte);    {get the next byte}
        SysExData := SysExData;    {check to see if it's data}
      END;
```

```
    END;
  END;{SysExData}


{───────────────────────────────────}
  FUNCTION GetMSNibble: longInt;
    VAR
      Y: integer;
  BEGIN
    ReadMIDI(Y);                       {get  byte with MS Nibble}
    IF SysExData = False THEN    {if it's not data,}
      GetMSNibble := DecodeERROR  {set decode error flag}
    ELSE
    BEGIN
      Y := BSL(Y, 4);                  {shift left 4 bits}
      GetMSNibble := Y;
    END;
  END; {GetMSNibble}


{───────────────────────────────────}
  FUNCTION GetMSBytes (size: integer): longint;
    VAR
      Y, Offset: integer;
      MSBits: longint;
  BEGIN
    FOR Offset := 1 TO Size - 1 DO
    BEGIN
      ReadMIDI(Y);                    {get  next byte}
      IF SysExData = False THEN   {if it's not data,}
      BEGIN
        GetMSBytes := DecodeERROR;{set decode error flag}
        Exit(GetMSBytes);             {return to calling routine}
      END
      ELSE
        MSBits := MSBits + BSL(Y, 7 * Offset);{shift left 7 and add}
    END;{For Offset ...}
    GetMSBytes := Y;{return MSbytes to calling routine}
  END; {GetMSBytes}


{───────────────────────────────────}
  FUNCTION GetSampleWord: longint;
    VAR
      X, Shift: integer;
      word: longint;
```

```
BEGIN
  word := 0;
  X := 0;
  shift := theDumpHdr.sformat;        {word size in bits}

  WHILE shift - 7 >= 7 DO
  BEGIN
    ReadMIDI(X);                      {get a byte}
    IF SysExData = False THEN
    BEGIN
      GetSampleWord := DecodeERROR;
      Exit(GetSampleWord);
    END;
    word := word + BSL(X, shift - 7); {shift left and add}
    shift := shift - 7;
  END;
  ReadMIDI(X);                        {get  last byte}
  IF SysExData = False THEN
  BEGIN
    GetSampleWord := DecodeERROR;
    Exit(GetSampleWord);
  END;
  IF shift > 0 THEN                   {if less than 7 bits remain}
    X := BSR(X, shift);               {shift right to LS bit}
  GetSampleWord := word + X;          {add MS bits and last byte}
END;{GetSampleWord}
{──────────────────────────────────────}
FUNCTION DecodeData (size, mode: integer): longint;
  VAR
    X, Y, Offset: integer;
    word: longint;
BEGIN
  ReadMIDI(X);                        {get  byte 1}
  IF SysExData = False THEN           {if it's not data,}
    DecodeData := DecodeERROR         {set decode error flag}
  ELSE
  BEGIN
    CASE mode OF
      LSNibbleMode:
      BEGIN
        Y := GetMSNibble; {get and shift MS Nibble}
        IF Y = DecodeERROR THEN       {if it's not data}
          DecodeData := DecodeERROR   {set decode error flag}
        ELSE
          DecodeData := X + Y;        {combine LS and MS nibbles}
      END; {LS Nibble}
```

```
    MSNibbleMode:
    BEGIN
      ReadMIDI(Y);                {get byte with LS Nibble}
      IF SysExData = False THEN      {if it's not data,}
        DecodeData := DecodeERROR    {set decode error flag}
      ELSE
      BEGIN
        X := BSL(X, 4);          {shift MS Nibble}
        DecodeData := X + Y;     {combine LS and MS nibbles}
      END;
    END; {MS Nibble}

    LSByteMode:
    BEGIN
      word := GetMSBytes(size);
      IF word = DecodeERROR THEN      {if it's note data}
        DecodeData := DecodeERROR     {set decode error flag}
      ELSE
        DecodeData := X + Word;{combine LS and MS bytes}
    END; {LSByte}
   END;{Case mode...}
  END;{X is data}
 END;{DecodeData}

{————————————————————————————}
 PROCEDURE GetPunchInTime (punchType: integer);
  VAR
    dataWord: longint;
    X: integer;

 BEGIN
  WITH theSmpteEvent DO
  BEGIN
    eventType := punchType;     {get punch In/Out type}

    ReadMIDI(theMIDIByte);      {get hour/type (1 byte)}
    IF SysExData = False THEN
      Exit(GetPunchInTime);
    X := theMIDIByte;
    hours := BitAND(X, $1F);    {decode & store hours }
    TimeCodeType := BSL(theMIDIByte, 5); {decode and store}

    ReadMIDI(theMIDIByte);      {get minutes (1 byte)}
    IF SysExData = False THEN
      Exit(GetPunchInTime);
    minutes := theMIDIByte;
```

```
    ReadMIDI(theMIDIByte);        {get seconds (1 byte)}
    IF SysExData = False THEN
      Exit(GetPunchInTime);
    seconds := theMIDIByte;

    ReadMIDI(theMIDIByte);        {get frame (1 byte)}
    IF SysExData = False THEN
      Exit(GetPunchInTime);
    frame := theMIDIByte;

    ReadMIDI(theMIDIByte); {get fractional frames (1 byte)}
    IF SysExData = False THEN
      Exit(GetPunchInTime);
    fracFrames := theMIDIByte;

    dataWord := DecodeData(2, LSbyteMode);{get 2 byte event nr}
    IF dataWord = decodeERROR THEN
      Exit(GetPunchInTime);
    eventNumber := dataWord;
  END;
END; {GetPunchInTime}
{─────────────────────────────────}
PROCEDURE ProcessMTCSetUp;
BEGIN
  ReadMIDI(theMIDIByte);          {get sub-ID #2}
  IF SysExData = False THEN
    Exit(ProcessMTCSetUp);        {stop if byte isn't data}

  CASE theMIDIByte OF             {parse sub-ID #2}
    0:
      ;{Special}
    1, 2:
      GetPunchInTime(theMIDIByte); {Punch In/Out}
    3, 4:
      ; {Delete Punch In/Out}
    5, 6:
      ; {Event Start/Stop}
    7, 8:
      ; {Event Start/Stop + Info}
    9, $A:
      ; {Delete Event Start/Stop}
    $B:
      ; {Cue Points}
    $C:
      ;{Cue Points + Info}
```

```
    $D:
      ;{Delete Cue Points}
    $E:
      ;{Event Name in Info}
    OTHERWISE
      ; {unrecognized MTC sub-ID #2, do nothing}
  END; {Case for sub-ID #2}
END;{ProcessMTCSetUp}


{————————————————————————}


PROCEDURE GetLoopPoint;
  VAR
    dataWord: longint;
BEGIN
  BEGIN
    WITH theLoop DO
    BEGIN
      dataWord := DecodeData(2, LSbyteMode);{get 2 byte s number}
      IF dataWord = decodeERROR THEN
        Exit(GetLoopPoint);
      sNumber := dataWord;

      dataWord := DecodeData(2, LSbyteMode);{get 2 byte loop nr}
      IF dataWord = decodeERROR THEN
        Exit(GetLoopPoint);
      loopNumber := dataWord;

      ReadMIDI(theMIDIByte);              {loop type (1 byte)}
      IF SysExData = False THEN
        Exit(GetLoopPoint);
      loopType := theMIDIByte;

      dataWord := DecodeData(3, LSbyteMode);{get 3 byte loop start}
      IF dataWord = decodeERROR THEN
        Exit(GetLoopPoint);
      loopStart := dataWord;

      dataWord := DecodeData(2, LSbyteMode);{get 3 byte loop end}
      IF dataWord = decodeERROR THEN
        Exit(GetLoopPoint);
      loopEnd := dataWord;
    END;
  END; {Case theMIDIByte}
END;{GetDeviceID}
```

```
{————————————————}
  PROCEDURE ProcessSDExt;
  BEGIN
    ReadMIDI(theMIDIByte);            {get sub-ID #2}
    IF SysExData = False THEN
      Exit(ProcessSDExt);             {stop if byte isn't data}

    CASE theMIDIByte OF               {parse sub-ID #2}
      1:
        ; {Multiple Loop Points}
      2:
        ; {Loop Points Request}

      OTHERWISE
        ; {unrecognized SD Extension sub-ID #2, do nothing}
    END; {Case for sub-ID #2}
  END;{ProcessSDExt}
{————————————————}
  PROCEDURE GetDeviceID;
  BEGIN
    ReadMIDI(theMIDIByte); {Manufacturer ID (1 byte)}
    IF SysExData = False THEN
      Exit(GetDeviceID);

    CASE theMIDIByte OF
      KorgID:            {only interested in Korg IDs}
      BEGIN
        WITH theKorgDevice DO
        BEGIN
          familyCode := DecodeData(2, LSbyteMode);{get family-2 bytes}
          IF familyCode = decodeERROR THEN
            Exit(GetDeviceID);

          memberCode := DecodeData(2, LSbyteMode);{get member-2 bytes}
          IF memberCode = decodeERROR THEN
            Exit(GetDeviceID);

          ROMCode := DecodeData(2, LSbyteMode);{get ROM nr-2 bytes}
          IF ROMCode = decodeERROR THEN
            Exit(GetDeviceID);

          softVersion := DecodeData(2, LSbyteMode);{get versn-2 bytes}
          IF softVersion = decodeERROR THEN
            Exit(GetDeviceID);
        END; {with the KorgDevice}
      END; {KorgID}
```

```
      OTHERWISE
         ; {manufacturer ID not recognized by application}
      END; {Case theMIDIByte}
    END;{GetDeviceID}
{———————————————————————————}
    PROCEDURE ProcessDevInquiry;
    BEGIN
      ReadMIDI(theMIDIByte);              {get sub-ID #2}
      IF SysExData = False THEN
        Exit(ProcessDevInquiry);          {stop if byte isn't data}

      CASE theMIDIByte OF                 {parse sub-ID #2}
        1:
           ; {Device ID Request}
        2:
           ; {Device ID Resply}
        OTHERWISE
           ; {unrecognized Device Inquiry sub-ID #2, do nothing}
      END; {Case for sub-ID #2}
    END;{ProcessDevInquiry}
{———————————————————————————}
    PROCEDURE GetSDHeader;
      VAR
        dataWord: longInt;
    BEGIN
      WITH theDumpHdr DO
      BEGIN
        dataWord := DecodeData(2, LSbyteMode);{get 2 byte s nr}
        IF dataWord = decodeERROR THEN
          Exit(GetSDHeader);  {stop if word isn't valid data}
        sNumber := dataWord; {load value into dhdr record}

        ReadMIDI(theMIDIByte);        {get sample format (1 byte)}
        IF SysExData = False THEN
          Exit(GetSDHeader);
        sFormat := theMIDIByte;

        dataWord := DecodeData(3, LSbyteMode);{get s period-3 bytes}
        IF dataWord = decodeERROR THEN
          Exit(GetSDHeader);
        sPeriod := dataWord;

        dataWord := DecodeData(3, LSbyteMode);{get s length-3 bytes}
        IF dataWord = decodeERROR THEN
          Exit(GetSDHeader);
        sLength := dataWord;
```

```
    dataWord := DecodeData(3, LSbyteMode);{get s loop start-3 bytes}
    IF dataWord = decodeERROR THEN
      Exit(GetSDHeader);
    susStart := dataWord;

    dataWord := DecodeData(2, LSbyteMode);{get s loop end-3 bytes}
    IF dataWord = decodeERROR THEN
      Exit(GetSDHeader);
    susEnd := dataWord;

    ReadMIDI(theMIDIByte);                    {get loop type (1 byte)}
    IF SysExData = False THEN
      Exit(GetSDHeader);
    loopType := theMIDIByte;
  END;
END;{GetSDHeader}
{————————————————————————————————}
PROCEDURE ProcessNonRealSysEx;
BEGIN
  ReadMIDI(theMIDIByte);          {get device ID byte}
  IF SysExData = False THEN
    Exit(ProcessNonRealSysEx);  {stop if byte isn't data}

  IF (theMIDIByte <> 127) AND (theMIDIByte <> myDevID) THEN
    Exit(ProcessNonRealSysEx);{stop if device ID mismatch}

  ReadMIDI(theMIDIByte);                {get sub-ID #1}
  IF SysExData = False THEN
    Exit(ProcessNonRealSysEx);  {stop if byte isn't data}

  CASE theMIDIByte OF                   {parse sub-ID #1}
    1:
      GetSDHeader; {process SD Header}
    2:
      ; {process SD Data Packet}
    3:
      ; {process SD Request}
    4:
      ProcessMTCSetUp;    {process MIDI TIME CODE messages}
    5:
      ProcessSDExt;{process SAMPLE DUMP EXTENSION messages}
    6:
      ProcessDevInquiry; {process DEVICE INQUIRY messages}
    $7C:
      ; {process Wait}
```

```
   $7D:
     ; {process Cancel}
   $7E:
     ; {process ACK}
   $7F:
     ; {process NAK}


   OTHERWISE
     ;{unrecognized sub-ID #1, do nothing}
   END; {Case for Non-Real-Time sub-ID #1}
 END; {ProcessNonRealSysEx}
{————————————————————————}
 PROCEDURE GetFullMessage;
   VAR
     X: integer;

BEGIN
  WITH theSmpteTime DO
  BEGIN
    ReadMIDI(theMIDIByte);        {get hour/type}
    IF SysExData = False THEN
      Exit(GetFullMessage);
    X := theMIDIByte;
    hours := BitAND(X, $1F);      {decode & store hours }
    TimeCodeType := BSL(theMIDIByte, 5); {decode & store TC type}

    ReadMIDI(theMIDIByte);        {get minutes }
    IF SysExData = False THEN
      Exit(GetFullMessage);
    minutes := theMIDIByte;

    ReadMIDI(theMIDIByte);        {get seconds}
    IF SysExData = False THEN
      Exit(GetFullMessage);
    seconds := theMIDIByte;

    ReadMIDI(theMIDIByte);        {get frame }
    IF SysExData = False THEN
      Exit(GetFullMessage);
    frame := theMIDIByte;
  END;
END;{GetFullMessage}
```

```
PROCEDURE GetUserBits;
  VAR
    X: integer;
BEGIN
  WITH theUserBits DO
  BEGIN
    X := DecodeData(2, MSNibbleMode);  {get user char 1-2 bytes}
    IF X = decodeERROR THEN
      Exit(GetUserBits);
    user1 := X;

    X := DecodeData(2, MSNibbleMode);  {get user char 2-2 bytes}
    IF X = decodeERROR THEN
      Exit(GetUserBits);
    user2 := X;

    X := DecodeData(2, MSNibbleMode);  {get user char 3-2 bytes}
    IF X = decodeERROR THEN
      Exit(GetUserBits);
    user3 := X;

    X := DecodeData(2, MSNibbleMode);  {get user char 4-2 bytes}
    IF X = decodeERROR THEN
      Exit(GetUserBits);
    user4 := X;

    ReadMIDI(theMIDIByte);                {get user Flags}
    IF SysExData = False THEN
      Exit(GetUserBits);
    userFlag1 := BTST(theMIDIByte, 0);
    userFlag2 := BTST(theMIDIByte, 1);
  END;
END;{GetUserBits}

{————————————————————————————————}
  PROCEDURE ProcessMTC;
  BEGIN
    ReadMIDI(theMIDIByte);          {get sub-ID #2}
    IF SysExData = False THEN
      Exit(ProcessMTC);             {stop if byte isn't data}
```

```
  CASE theMIDIByte OF               {parse sub-ID #2}
    1:
      GetFullMessage; {Full Message}
    2:
      GetUserBits; {User Bits}
    OTHERWISE
      ; {unrecognized MTC sub-ID #2, do nothing}
  END; {Case for sub-ID #2}
END;{ProcessMTC}


{────────────────────────────────}
  PROCEDURE ProcessRealSysEx;
  BEGIN
    ReadMIDI(theMIDIByte);          {get device ID byte}
    IF SysExData = False THEN
      Exit(ProcessRealSysEx);       {stop if byte isn't data}

    IF (theMIDIByte <> 127) AND (theMIDIByte <> myDevID) THEN
      Exit(ProcessRealSysEx);       {stop if device ID mismatch}

    ReadMIDI(theMIDIByte);          {get sub-ID #1}
    IF SysExData = False THEN
      Exit(ProcessRealSysEx);       {stop if byte isn't data}

    CASE theMIDIByte OF             {parse sub-ID #1}
      1:
        ProcessMTC; {process MIDI TIME CODE}
      OTHERWISE
        ;{unrecognized Real Time sub-ID #1, do nothing}
    END; {Case for sub-ID #1}
  END; {ProcessRealSysEx}

{────────────────────────────────}
  PROCEDURE Process3ByteID;
  BEGIN
    ReadMIDI(theMIDIByte);          {get ID #1}
    IF SysExData = False THEN
      Exit(Process3ByteID);{stop if byte isn't data}

    CASE theMIDIByte OF             {parse ID #1}
      0:
      BEGIN
        ReadMIDI(theMIDIByte);      {get ID #2}
        IF SysExData = False THEN
          Exit(Process3ByteID);     {stop if byte isn't data}
```

```
      CASE theMIDIByte OF        {parse ID #2}

        $07:
          ; {process Digital Music Corp SysEx}
        $0B:
          ; {process IVL Technologies SysEx}
        $10:
          ; {process DOD SysEx}
        OTHERWISE
          ; {unrecognized Manufacture ID #2, do nothing}
      END; {Case for ID #2}
    END; {ID 1 = 0 block}
    OTHERWISE
      ;{unrecognized ID #1, do nothing}
  END; {Case for ID #1}
END;{Process3ByteID}

{————————————————————————————————}
  PROCEDURE GetM1ParameterChange;
  VAR
    dataWord: longint;

BEGIN
  WITH theM1Parameter DO
  BEGIN
    ReadMIDI(theMIDIByte);              {get page}
    IF SysExData = False THEN
      Exit(GetM1ParameterChange);       {stop if not data}
    page := theMIDIByte;

    ReadMIDI(theMIDIByte);              {get position}
    IF SysExData = False THEN
      Exit(GetM1ParameterChange);       {stop if not data}
    position := theMIDIByte;

    dataWord := DecodeData(2, LSbyteMode);{get 2 bytes-LSB 1st}
    IF value = decodeERROR THEN
      Exit(GetM1ParameterChange); {stop if word not valid data}
    value := dataWord;
  END;
END;{GetM1ParameterChange}
```

```
PROCEDURE ProcessKorgSysEx;
BEGIN
  ReadMIDI(theMIDIByte);          {get Korg format ID}
  IF (SysExData = False) OR (theMIDIBYTE <> KorgFormatID) THEN
    Exit(ProcessKorgSysEx);       {stop if not Korg format ID}

  ReadMIDI(theMIDIByte);          {get M1 ID}
  IF (SysExData = False) OR (theMIDIBYTE <> M1_ID) THEN
    Exit(ProcessKorgSysEx);       {stop if not M1 ID}

  ReadMIDI(theMIDIByte); {get M1 function code}
  IF SysExData = False THEN
    Exit(ProcessKorgSysEx);       {stop if byte isn't data}


  CASE theMIDIByte OF             {M1 function code}

    $21..$24, $26:
      ; {handshaking messages}
    $40:
      ; {program dump}
    $41:
      GetM1ParameterChange;
    $42:
      ; {mode data}
    $45:
      ; {all multi sound(PCM Card)name}
    $47:
      ; {all drum sound(PCM Card)name}
    $48:
      ; {all sequence data dump}
    $49:
      ; {combination parameter dump}
    $50:
      ;{all data (GLB,CMB,PRG,SEQ) dump}
    $51:
      ; {global data dump}
    OTHERWISE
      ; {unrecognized M1 function code, report error}
  END; {Case for function code}
END;{ProcessKorgSysEx}
```

```
PROCEDURE ProcessSysEx;
BEGIN
  ReadMIDI(theMIDIByte);          {get SysEx byte 2 }
  IF SysExData = False THEN
    Exit(ProcessSysEx);           {stop if byte isn't data}

  CASE theMIDIByte OF             {parse SysEx byte 2}
    0:
      Process3ByteID;
    $06:
      ; {process Lexicon SysEx}
    $07:
      ; {process Kurzweil SysEx}
    $41:
      ; {process Roland SysEx}
    $42:
      ProcessKorgSysEx;
    $7E:
      ProcessNonRealSysEx;
    $7F:
      ProcessRealSysEx;
    OTHERWISE
      ; {SysEx type is not recognized, do nothing}
  END;
END;{ProcessSysEx}

{—————————————————————————}
  PROCEDURE UpdateStatus;
  BEGIN
    CASE theMIDIByte OF

      NoteOff1..PitchWheel16: {range of all Channel status messages}
      BEGIN
        statusBuffer := theMIDIByte;{assign status to statusBuffer}
        dataCount := 0;     {new status, reset value of dataCount}
      END;

      SysEx:
      BEGIN                      {call SysEx processing routine}
        IF SysExFlag THEN
          ProcessSysEx;
        statusBuffer := Ignore;{clear after processing or if ignored}
        dataCount := 0;     {new status, reset value of dataCount}
      END; {Call Note processing routine}
```

```
      QFrame..EOX:{range of all non SysEx System Common messages}
      BEGIN
        statusBuffer := Ignore;   {ignore these messages for now}
        dataCount := 0;      {new status, reset value of dataCount}
      END;


      OTHERWISE {theMIDIByte must be a Real-Time status byte}
      BEGIN
        ;                    {process System Real Time bytes here}
        ReadMIDI(theMIDIByte);     {get the next MIDI byte}
        IF theMIDIByte >= NoteOff1 THEN {check if a status byte}
          UpdateStatus;      {if it is, update the status buffer}
      END;
    END; {CASE theMIDIByte}
  END; {UpdateStatusBuffer}


{──────────────────────────────────────────}
  PROCEDURE FilterChannels;
    VAR
      channelNumber: integer;
  BEGIN
    channelNumber := GetChannel(theMIDIByte);
    IF Channel[channelNumber] = -1 THEN
      statusBuffer := ignore;
  END;{FilterChannels}


{──────────────────────────────────────────}
  PROCEDURE ProcessChannels;
    VAR
      channelNumber: integer;
  BEGIN
    channelNumber := GetChannel(theMIDIByte);
    IF Channel[channelNumber] = -1 THEN
      statusBuffer := ignore
    ELSE
      theMIDIByte := BitAND(theMIDIByte, $F0) +
Channel[channelNumber];
  END;{ProcessChannels}
```

The ParseMIDI procedure is divided into two main blocks. This}
first block parses each byte as status of data. Data bytes are}
passed on to the next block. Status bytes are passed to the}
UpdateStatus procedure where the status buffer is set or cleared.}
System Message bytes are processed {from within this block (via}
UpdateStatus). All status and data bytes for channel messages are}
passed to the second block. The a case structure parses each byte}
according to the current value of the status buffer.A case-}
statement for each recoginized status type calls the appropriate}
message processing routines. Processing of messages handled by }
each case-statement is enbaled/disabled with a flag variable.}

```
  PROCEDURE ParseMIDI;
  BEGIN
{Parse status/data and process System Messages}
    IF theMIDIByte >= NoteOff1 THEN {parse status from data bytes}
    BEGIN
      UpdateStatus;                        {update buffer if
necessary}
      IF (theMIDIByte < SysEx) AND (ChannelFlag) THEN
        ProcessChannels;    {Call Channel processing routine}
    END;

{Parse Channel Message bytes and processing recognized messages}
    CASE statusBuffer OF          {process byte based on status}
      Ignore:
        ; {do nothing with unrecognized status or data bytes}
   {call processing routines for recognized status types}

      NoteOff1..NoteOn16:
        IF NoteFlag THEN
   {Call Note processing routine}
        ELSE
        BEGIN
          statusBuffer := Ignore;
          dataCount := 0;
        END; {Call Note processing routine}

      PolyPress1..PolyPress16:
        IF PPressFlag THEN
   {Call Poly Pressure processing routine}
        ELSE
        BEGIN
          statusBuffer := Ignore;
          dataCount := 0;
        END;
```

```
  ControlChange1..ControlChange16:
    IF CChangeFlag THEN
{Call Control Change processing routine}
    ELSE
    BEGIN
      statusBuffer := Ignore;
      dataCount := 0;
    END;

  ProgramChange1..ProgramChange16:
    IF PChangeFlag THEN
{Call P Change processing routine}
    ELSE
    BEGIN
      statusBuffer := Ignore;
      dataCount := 0;
    END;

  ChanPress1..ChanPress16:
    IF CPressFlag THEN
{Call Channel Pressure processing routine}
    ELSE
    BEGIN
      statusBuffer := Ignore;
      dataCount := 0;
    END;

  PitchWheel1..PitchWheel16:
    IF PWheelFlag THEN
{Call P Wheel processing routine}
    ELSE
    BEGIN
      statusBuffer := Ignore;
      dataCount := 0;
    END;

  OTHERWISE
    ; {bytes belong to unrecognized status, do nothing}
  END;{CASE statusBuffer}
END; {ParseMIDI}
```

```
PROCEDURE ThruLoop;
BEGIN
  WHILE ThruFlag DO
  BEGIN
    ReadMIDI(theMIDIByte);         {get a byte from MIDI In port}
    ParseMIDI;                     {parse and process the byte}
    IF statusBuffer <> Ignore THEN     {if it's recognized data,}
      WriteMIDI(theMIDIByte);      {send byte to MIDI Out port}
  END; {WHILE TRUE}
END; {ThruLoop}

END.{MIDIThruProcs}
```

About the Authors

Steve De Furia

Joe Scacciaferro

Steve De Furia is on the executive board of the MIDI Manufacturer's Association and is a columnist for *Keyboard* magazine. He is an active studio musician and synthesist with numerous album, film, and session credits. He got his start as a computer programmer by writing music composition software for Frank Zappa. Steve is also the co-author of a series of music technology books, including *MIDI Programming for the Macintosh* (M&T Books, 1988).

Joe Scacciaferro is an electrical engineer and president of Triple S Electronics, the nation's largest service and design facility for computer-based musical instruments. He is also a columnist for *Music, Computers, and Software* magazine and co-author of a series of music technology books, including *MIDI Programming for the Macintosh* (M&T Books, 1988).

Index

More MIDI Books from M&T Books

MIDI Programmer's Handbook

by Steve DeFuria and Joe Scacciaferro of Ferro Technologies

The *MIDI Programmer's Handbook* is a complete and indispensible reference for anyone writing MIDI programs. It is the ideal resource for programmers and musicians currently programming MIDI applications. And because it is not specific to any computer system or language it is equally useful to IBM, Atari, Commodore, and Apple programmers. Authors DeFuria and Scacciaferro begin with an overview of MIDI as a communication standard then move on to a detailed investigation of the make-up, contents, and implications of every currently defined MIDI message. Also presented is a look into the different ways MIDI is implemented in commercial devices, with a focus on what programmers can expect to find when writing software to interact with commercial MIDI devices. Finally, the authors present various examples of how to approach specific MIDI related tasks from within a program. Basic and Pascal routines are used to illustrate the concepts and techniques. These routines make up a "toolbox" of MIDI functions that can be transported onto any computer in any language.

Book & Disk (MS-DOS, Macintosh, Atari)   *Item #068-0*   *$39.99*
Book only   *Item #069-9*   *$24.95*

C Programming for MIDI

by Jim Conger

Both musicians and programmers can learn how to create useful programs and libraries of software tools for music applications. Outlined are the features of MIDI and its support of real-time access to musical devices. An introduction to C programming fundamentals as they relate to MIDI is provided. These concepts are fully demonstrated with two MIDI applications: a patch librarian and a simple sequencer. Some of the fundamental MIDI programming elements you'll learn are: full development of a patch librarian program, sequencing applications for the MPU-401 interface, how to create screen displays, and how to write low-level assembly language routines for MIDI. *C Programming for MIDI* shows you how to write customized programs to create the sounds and effects you need. All programs are available on disk with full source code. Supports both Microsoft C and Turbo C.

Book & Disk (MS-DOS)   *Item #90-9*   *$37.95*
Book only   *Item #86-0*   *$22.95*

More MIDI Tools ...

MIDI Programming for the Macintosh

Steve De Furia and Joe Scacciaferro of Ferro Technologies

This book equips musicians and programmers with the background necessary to program music applications and take advantage of all that the Macintosh and MIDI interface have to offer. Authors De Furia and Scacciaferro begin with an excellent introduction to MIDI and Macintosh programming, covering such topics as MIDI devices (hardware and software), the Macintosh user interface, program design, Macintosh programming languages and tools, and MIDI code resources.

The authors then delve into programming applications presenting the basics of programming the Macintosh's ROM-based toolbox and giving the reader a set of software tools that can be used and expanded upon in any Macintosh application. The final sections present guidelines for creating one's own software. All the programs are available on an optional disk with full source code and compiled applications and resource files.

Book & Disk   *Item #022-2 $37.95*
Book   *Item #021-4 $22.95*

MIDI and Sound Book for the Atari ST

Bernd Enders and Wolfgang Klemme

Find out why the Atari ST is one of the hottest MIDI computers available and how to make it work. This book provides you with an introduction to the acoustic and musical basics of sound sythesis and sound chip programming. With a detailed description of MIDI technology, you can learn to utilize MIDI functions to suit your specific needs.

Along with a discussion of commercially marketed samplers, the *MIDI and Sound Book for the Atari ST* contains an assembler routine plus a hardware description of a do-it-yourself 8-bit converter. A GFA-Basic program on the optional disk provides a short introduction to music theory-notes, sounds, keys, and intervals. Other example programs are also included on disk.

Book & Disk (Atari)   *Item #043-5 $34.95*
Book   *Item #042-7 $17.95*

More MIDI Tools ...

MIDI Sequencing in C

Jim Conger

Picking up where his popular book *C Programming for MIDI* left off, Jim Conger's *MIDI Sequencing in C* approaches the recording and playback of MIDI data from the perspective of both users and programmers. The first few chapters provide a tutorial, describing the multi-track sequencer from the user's point of view. The remaining chapters describe how the program works. Covered are such topics as program documenation, higher-level video functions, the multi-track eight-track MIDI recorder, measure level editing functions, note level editing, and file and utility functions.

The optional disk is highly recommended. For the non-programmer there is a ready-to-use eight-track MIDI sequencer with editing features. For the developing programmer the source code for the multi-track sequencer follows the programming examples in *C Programming for MIDI* and expands them into a full application. This can serve as a starting point for experiments and additions to the basic MT program. For the experienced programmer, the source code provides functions that can be applied to a wide range of MIDI projects.

The program will run on IBM PCs, ATs, or equivalent computers using the Roland MPU-401 MIDI interface (or equivalent).

Book & Disk   ***Item #046-X***   ***$39.95***
Book   ***Item #045-1***   ***$24.95***